PERSO

AND STRESS

finding ways to manage your stress

PERSONALITY
AND STRESS

finding ways to manage your stress

RUTH FOWKE

CWR

The author is kindly donating all royalties from this book to Feba Radio.

CONTENTS

PREFACE

A little neglect may breed mischief … for want of a nail, the
shoe was lost; for want of a shoe, the horse was lost; for want
of a horse, the rider was lost …

Benjamin Franklin

This book was originally published in 2000 under the title of *The Last
Straw*. Not long afterwards, the publishing company sadly went out of
business – ironically, they had met their last straw. So I was delighted
when CWR suggested doing it as a companion book to *Personality
and Prayer* under the present title which is equally applicable. What
is the last straw for one person often leaves someone with a different
personality completely unscathed.

Dealing with small problems as we notice them saves
considerable trouble later. 'A stitch in time saves nine' is a proverb that
was often quoted in the days before our contemporary throwaway age.

Attending to the minor pinpricks of daily life helps to forestall
the build-up of major troubles. As a doctor I am primarily concerned
with prevention. That means paying attention to the roots of a
problem, rather than always dealing with the end result. It is
obviously more effective to prevent a fire from starting than to put it
out when it is already raging.

Stress affects us all at various times, and in different ways. Some
are more afflicted than others, but no one is immune. Apparently
small issues often build up and contribute to the sense of stress
that plagues so many today. It is important to note what ruffles our
feathers, what needles and provokes us in small matters, and then
do something about it.

This book is designed to help people recognise their early signs
of stress, so that they will be able to make appropriate modifications
in their own lifestyle, and enjoy more of life.

There is a sense in which stress is a normal and absolutely

necessary part of life. When it is taken to mean a force exerting pressure which results in some action, then stress is vital. Being without stress in this sense would mean a life without any activity at all.

Engineers use the 'S' word in a more technical and precise way. They use it in the sense of applying force of some sort to a material, so that the material will bend or stretch, or behave in some other predictable and measurable way. The material will then return to its normal state when the stress is removed. When it is not removed at the critical point then the material snaps or breaks. There are parallels to that in human life, but it is not how I shall be using the term.

The word 'stimulation' and its derivatives are used to denote beneficial forces that spur us on to take appropriate action. The word 'stress' and its offshoots are employed in their ordinary, everyday usage. Stress is taken to mean a situation that is unpleasant and uncomfortable, and that places an undue strain upon the person. It denotes something that leads to distress.

Stress is generally undesirable, but not always so. Sometimes when a person realises that they are stressed it can prompt them to look at, and correct, assumptions and attitudes that are no longer necessary or appropriate to their stage in life.

Much of the material in this book is based on the various seminars and workshops on stress I have led in recent years. I am greatly indebted to the members who have taken part, and who have made valuable contributions to my thinking. Part Two would not have been possible without the many insights from, and incidents with, my friend and colleague Di Whitwam. The fact that she and I have opposite preferences in three of the four pairs of traits described (see Chapter 6) has been a rich experience.

I am grateful to other friends who have helped me, especially the three who generously read and commented on the first draft of this book.

Ruth Fowke, 2009

qui

9.30 interview
3pm me
all mum-
clean
8pm pick
Put up
wa
e i
spra
m
5?
8
ke

1. TAKE A BREAK

Violin and guitar players are careful to relax the tension in the strings of their instruments every time they cease to use them. In this way the vital strings are preserved. They are then ready to be stretched again when next needed. Kept taut, they would easily snap.

A rubber band does not keep its elasticity when it is constantly taut. It snaps or goes brittle, and has to be thrown out. In our complex society we have lost the rhythm of work followed by play; of toil needing to be succeeded by relaxation, and we need to regain this principle.

Generally speaking, any good and satisfying piece of work is followed by a momentary break. We shift our position in some way, to relax our muscles, so that they are ready for the next bit of work to be done. We do this quite automatically and unconsciously, in order to maintain our ability to carry on effectively for considerable periods.

When our work is not quite up to standard there is even more reason to follow this healthy routine. The chances are that even a mini-break will be followed by a much better result from the very next effort.

What most of us actually do is to follow the poor work with immediate greater effort, without even a minuscule break. The outcome is then even poorer. Lacking that brief respite, what we manage to do next is less effective. Output drops. The probability is that we then redouble our efforts, still without taking any restorative break. We get taut and strung up.

The more tense we are, the less we are prepared to take a break. We get distraught at not being able to achieve what we set out to do. So we have yet another go, still without a break. The more we need to take one, the less likely we are to do so. It is as though some internal pressure drives us on. This cycle is shown in Diagram 1.

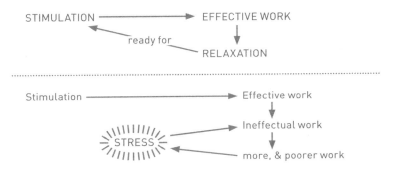

Diagram 1: Efficient and Inefficient Cycles

There are many variations on the story about a man chopping logs. It was getting dark, he was tired and there was still a large pile for him to do. A neighbour watched, then helpfully suggested that he would make more progress if he stopped and sharpened his axe. 'Can't stop,' the man grumbled. 'No time for things like that.' He was unwilling to stop his repetitive action and relax by doing something else. Because he did not take that small amount of time off, he needed to use more effort to get the job done. And it took longer.

When we are provoked, our bodies instinctively respond in a number of finely co-ordinated and interrelated ways. Together these are designed to enable us to deal with the situation. If we put a hand on a hot stove, or see a brick come hurtling towards us, we do not think out what to do. We automatically jerk our hand away or duck out of the line of fire. There are also immediate, involuntary changes that occur internally, and some of them are graphically portrayed in a number of common sayings.

It is no wonder we are 'sick with fright'. The vascular response to threat is to narrow the blood vessels in the stomach and intestines. This enables more blood to be sent to the muscles we are going to need in order to deal with the situation that has alarmed us. For the same reason we may go 'white as a sheet'. The blood flow in the face and areas of the body whose function is primarily maintenance is reduced. Blood is then redirected to those organs which are essential for emergency responses. It is especially increased in the lungs, brain and limb muscles.

Many more undetected back-up forces are also mobilised in the liver and various internal glands. They all go into action in a synchronised way to ensure that the body has the resources it needs to deal with the threat. The hormone balance is altered away from maintaining the status quo and directed towards releasing sugar and fats to provide energy. All this means that our bodies and minds are geared up into a state of high alert, ready for action. When the situation has been dealt with, and the alarm is shut off, both body and mind gradually return to their usual waking level. Muscles relax into their stand-by mode, and blood returns to the areas from which it was temporarily diverted.

The biological purpose for this complex set of internal responses is to enable the individual to either grapple with an aggressor or run for cover. This is the elementary 'fight or flight' response to danger. Civilised life means that in most situations we can rarely indulge in such direct action. Our natural responses are tamed, or shamed, out of awareness. There is no outward physical reaction to the challenge presented, but the internal responses still occur.

If the fats circulating in the blood vessels are not burned up they will get deposited on the walls of arteries, which will eventually become clogged. If the energy that has been mobilised is no longer used up in activity, then tension inevitably builds up. Stress symptoms may affect any organ or function of the body, depending on a mixture of genetic inheritance, personal vulnerability and perhaps a degree of individual prior conditioning.

It is important for people to become familiar with their own early warning signs of impending stress. When they recognise their own particular indicators they can take steps to deal with the situation while it is still manageable. In general, when people are getting tense they lose their sense of humour. Also, the ability to adapt easily to new situations is likely to be diminished. And, they probably get stuck in their own ways, with their normal characteristics becoming exaggerated. Tolerance of others is likely to be lessened. The people who are usually decisive tend to become more rigid in their views, and are likely to take up entrenched positions which they hold with great tenacity. Those who are more commonly indecisive are inclined to become even more wavering and hesitant.

In addition to these generalisations, many people adopt their own individual, sometimes idiosyncratic, behaviours when stressed. Years ago a friend told me that she always knew when I was bothered about something because I fiddled with my left earring. Never the right one, only the left. I did not believe her but that night I looked in the mirror and, sure enough, the hole in my left ear was twice as large as the one in the right. Now whenever my hand strays to my left ear lobe I ask myself what is bothering me, and try to do something more constructive about the issue.

As our reaction to stress is so very physical it is important that we take physical first aid measures to manage the symptoms. The breathing of most stressed people tends to become shallow and more rapid than normal. This results in an inadequate exchange of oxygen and carbon dioxide through the small blood vessels in the lining of the lungs. We therefore need to take conscious control of the process, deliberately breathing more deeply and slowly to correct the imbalance in blood gases. Such action helps to restore a feeling of calm. Try it next time you're getting steamed up when kept waiting in a queue, or your train is delayed.

When I worked in the NHS we used to have regular Hospital Management Committee meetings. During one seemingly endless meeting I realised, with sinking heart, that my bid for more departmental resources was not going well. I attempted to present the situation with greater urgency. A colleague realised that I was being more emotive than objective, and quietly whispered, 'Ruth, breathe'. I knew exactly what she meant and quietly took a few deep, measured breaths. That was all that was necessary to enable me to calm down, take stock, and resume with a more detached presentation of our case.

At the same time, a more relaxed attitude of mind can be achieved by adopting a more relaxed bodily posture. As well as paying attention to your breathing make sure you relax your jaw; the chances are that you are clenching your teeth. It is important for each individual to notice just where in their body they feel tense, so that they can relax that area. Sometimes this can be achieved paradoxically by first *increasing* the muscle tension there, holding that as long possible, and then letting go totally.

Some people find it helpful to practise this in private, alternately tensing their hands, then their feet, to maximum, and then letting them relax completely. After doing this a few times it is possible to feel a delightful sense of wellbeing spread to other areas of the body as you relax those few muscles, but it does take practice. When you have mastered the technique it is possible to employ it discreetly wherever you are.

Another effect of stress is that we get tunnel vision and cannot see beyond our own particular predicament. It engulfs us so that we cannot see the wood for the trees. In this state anything that helps us to adjust our focus is beneficial. We can help ourselves to refocus our thinking by physically changing the focus of our eyes. By momentarily glancing as far away as you can from the accounts that will not balance, or the people who seem to be being obstructive, you can often get a better perspective on how to handle the situation.

It is worth being disciplined enough to break off from your preoccupation, and look out of the window at the horizon. At the very least, gaze at the furthest corner of the room for a few seconds. Even a momentary change in eye focus really can help you to also re-focus your mind. Try it next time you realise that something, or someone, is getting under your skin.

The maxim 'Don't just sit there, do something' is an excellent one whenever you feel tension creeping up on you. Walk just a few steps to adjust the window, pick up a book or fetch some papers (even if you do not really need them at that moment). This is a good way of discharging the tautness that is beginning to build up in your mind and in your muscles. Such action also serves as a mini-break from the matter in hand. It provides a short interval that enables you to come back to the situation in better shape to address it more effectively. The situation has not changed, but you have. Not much, it's true, but hopefully just enough to make the difference between handling or mis-handling whatever is causing you concern.

As well as making sure that you breathe slowly, deeply and rhythmically, take a look out of the window and walk about a bit, you can employ another useful first aid measure. This is to deliberately behave in the opposite way to whatever powerful but unhelpful feelings you may be experiencing. Whenever you feel angry, antagonistic, hostile or exasperated, acknowledge this to yourself but smile at your adversary. Smile instead of scowling. It is much more effective. Pass him the jug of water, smiling as you do so, instead of mentally throwing it over him, or shoving it along the table and leaving it just out of reach. To use a personal illustration, being late is one of my pressure points. However, now when I find I have put myself under stress by leaving late I find it helpful to behave as if I have all the time in the world. Rather than driving along in the car wanting to terrorise pedestrians who meander across the road, I have discovered that by slowing down and waving them across with a smile, I soon begin to smile inside as well as on the outside. Slowly, I cease to seethe inside. Many pedestrians are so surprised that they smile and wave back, reinforcing my rising good mood. My journey takes only marginally, if at all, longer and I arrive at my destination in a much better frame of mind. (The real solution is to allow more journey time in the first place!) The matter of time pressures is discussed in Chapter 8.

It is vitally important that we never disown our emotions.

If we do, they are sure to go underground and cause havoc in the future. We can, however, make a deliberate choice to behave in a way that is diametrically opposite to them. While doing so, it is essential that we acknowledge our feelings. By acknowledging our destructive feelings (to ourselves), we are recognising that they are a force that needs to be sympathetically explored at a more opportune time. It may be adequate to talk the episode through with a friend or colleague, but if you notice a repeated pattern in yourself you may need more assistance. A counsellor or pastoral worker may be able to help you unravel what precipitates you into certain reactions. This takes time and patience. Meanwhile, as you keep employing the first aid measures outlined above you will become more proficient in their use. It is a matter of working on both ends at once. Tackle the consequences of your reaction to a particular stress (behaviour), and the personal meaning (why it gets to you), at the same time. The behavioural aspect is sometimes the more accessible, which is why it is important to make changes there. At the same time, or subsequently, it will be wise to explore the emotional component.

It is never productive to blame an outside source for our own reactions. To say anything akin to 'He always winds me up' is shifting the blame and portraying ourselves as powerless. It is far better to take responsibility for our own actions. Say something like 'I always seem to get wound up when ...', or 'I let myself get mad whenever ...'. By making an 'I' statement like this we are putting the onus on ourselves. It opens up the possibility for us to explore our own reactions to any particular trigger. That is a useful thing to do, for we shall most surely meet a similar situation again.

For the Christian, noticing the reactions that disturb us is something to be talked over with the Lord of our lives. It is a matter for inclusion in a review of the day, or at some other regular time of prayer. It is always important not to neglect such a source of growth and grace, as we seek to find a way of dealing with powerful and inexplicable emotions. Sometimes, by noticing the pattern of events and our reactions to them, we can pick up clues about what is going on within. Until we can deal with some root causes we will continually only be pulling up the shoots that spring from them. In Chapter 4 we will look more closely at some of the background situations that may make us predisposed to react vigorously to certain trigger situations.

Today the things that threaten us are seldom ones calling for a simple 'fight or flight' measure. Despite this, the psychological and physiological responses remain the same. Our bodies and minds are geared up for action, but there is no direct way to deal with many of the situations that confront us daily. Although the basic responses are no longer appropriate, the body still mobilises its reserves in the same way. Energy continues to accumulate ready for action, and some alternative way of discharging it has to be found if stress symptoms are to be avoided.

We cannot avoid stress, so we must learn to utilise the energy it generates. When we become irritated in the office it is usually unwise to give direct vent to the anger we experience, and so we have to find an alternative that is more acceptable than 'kicking the cat'. We must each find our own way of displacing the energy aroused, and discharging it in an acceptable way. For example, constructive destruction in the garden, such as tackling overgrown areas, works wonders. So does pitching in to previously neglected chores about the house. Such activity has a visible result which in itself is rewarding, and the energy expended works off some of the accumulated frustration.

Those who participate in active sports, or who can regularly work off their pent-up feelings on the allotment, know how very much better they feel afterwards. Many people in sedentary occupations find that a good work-out in the gym, jogging regularly or swimming during the lunch break is beneficial. It is good for their general health, and it increases their ability to tolerate the inevitable stresses of life.

Stress First Aid

1. Breath control. Take a few deep, slow rhythmical breaths, then breathe easily again.
2. Re-focus your eyes to the most distant point. Look at the horizon, or the furthest corner of the room.
3. DO something. Walk round the room or shuffle in your chair.
4. Take a mini-break.
5. Counter-act; smile at your adversary.
6. Remember Jesus loves you. Smile with Him.
7. As soon as you can, take a longer break. Do something physical and enjoyable.
8. Laughter is a great way to relax. Share a joke with a friend. Look at some cartoons.
9. Accept the invitation of Jesus to 'Come with me by your[self] to a quiet place and get some rest' (Mark 6:31).

2. STRAWS IN THE WIND

It is seldom the big issues that cause us to stumble and fall or to blow our top. More often it is the persistent little irritants that won't go away. They tend to accumulate until their combined weight is just too much to carry or endure. Even camels, those desert beasts of burden, have their limit. It is not the first few bundles put upon a camel, but the last little one, the last straw, that proverbially breaks its back.

We may not be able to do much about some of the burdens we carry at different stages of our lives. We can, however, deal with many of the straws that tend to settle on top of the bigger burdens. The seemingly small things in life are often the ones that are actually most crucial. Lacking a nail, the shoe came off the horse. As a result, the horse and its rider were both lost. Any individual item may be so small that we are inclined to dismiss its significance when we are feeling under pressure. Its importance lies in the fact that when we can bring ourselves to deal with each matter as it arises, we spare ourselves the knock-on effects. When we remove a few straws from the camel's back it will not break and we can carry on. When we replace the nail, the shoe will stay on the horse and neither it nor the rider will be lost.

I have come across two prayers that are appropriate in such instances. One says simply, 'O Lord, either strengthen my back, or lighten my load'. The other is Reinhold Niebuhr's Serenity Prayer:

> God, give us grace to accept with serenity
> the things that cannot be changed,
> Courage to change the things
> that should be changed,
> And the Wisdom to distinguish
> the one from the other.
> Amen

Someone once guesstimated that only 20 per cent of our experiences are beyond our control. That person held that we can influence 30 per cent of what happens to us by asking for the help of others. The remaining 50 per cent are things that we ourselves can do something about. That 50 per cent is going to be our primary concern. The 30 per cent that we can modify with the help of others is also of great importance.

It takes both courage and humility to ask for help. When we choose to take that decisive step we must ensure that we are seeking the right assistance from the relevant person. When I was working as a doctor I was surprised how frequently some people seemed to take their medical troubles to the social worker, spiritual doubts to their doctor and social problems to the vicar. I also noticed that those were the people generally most likely to complain that no one ever helped them! We cannot expect our situation to improve unless we first accurately discern what is wrong, and then set about seeking, and evaluating, the appropriate advice. Furthermore, our attitude to those things that really are beyond our control will be pivotal. Attitude may not alter our circumstances, but it does affect how we live our lives. It determines how we act, and react, to everything, all the time.

It is important to detect early signs of stress, and to discover quite precisely what particular straws may be contributing to the overall load we are carrying. When we know this then we can set about finding ways of removing those straws that can be removed, and of effectively managing the stress that really is an inevitable part of life at the moment. This last point is important. Most people can cope with stress when it is a more or less temporary extra burden that they are being asked to shoulder. It is when there is no foreseeable end to the load they are carrying that the knees of many people tend to buckle, and eventually break. For this reason, even short times of respite are vital to enable a person to carry on. Such interludes are especially valuable when they are regular and can be relied upon.

Stimulation is necessary for life, but stress weakens the capacity to live life to the full. We need to be stimulated in order to swing into action, but we can have too much of even a good thing. When the stimulus, or stimuli, get too much or go on for too long for any individual then it ceases to stimulate. Instead it begins to become stressful. On the other hand, too little stimulation and we rust out, due to inertia. Just the right amount prompts us to a suitable work-out that is both effective and efficient.

There comes a time when, if there is no break from the stimulation, it ceases to be fruitful. When it is unremitting in duration or amount, then productivity actually falls despite an increase in the effort being expended. It is at this stage that a person may be heading for burn-out. When such a decline is detected, and appropriate remedial action is taken in time, then incapacity can usually be avoided. We look at this in Chapter 3.

Whether or not an individual becomes stressed will depend upon a number of variable factors. It is determined by the context in which things are happening, how vulnerable the person is at the time, and the type of experience they are having.

Firstly, context is important. Most of us can withstand greater pressure in some situations than we can tolerate in others, depending on our training, and on our expectations of that specific background. We are trained to respond with forbearance to even the most trying colleague or customer at work. At home, however, the merest hint of any disagreement may indeed prove to be the last straw, especially when we are tired. On the other hand, moral lapses may seem more shocking when they occur amongst colleagues at work than when we hear of them in a social context, or the other way around. Our understanding of what is, and is not, acceptable behaviour is quite different in the two different settings; we just do not reckon that 'that sort of person' will do 'that sort of thing' in that particular scenario.

Our individual vulnerability at any given time is also an important factor. All of us are less resilient during illness and in the subsequent recovery phase. We are particularly vulnerable at those times when we are emotionally depleted, whatever the reason for that state may be. Prolonged fatigue is another potent reason for lowered resistance to stress, although it often becomes accepted as 'just part of life' and so goes unchallenged and uncorrected.

Regarding different types of experience, something which arouses and thrills one person may be a considerable stress to another. Some, for example, are excited by the challenge of motor racing (on or off a recognised track!) while others find even driving in a quiet country town both tiresome and demanding. The Chinese have a proverb to the effect that two-thirds of what we 'see' is actually behind our own eyes. It is how the individual construes a situation and interprets it in the light of his or her particular background that determines whether or not he or she finds it stressful.

Another influence to be considered is the differing effect that change has on people. Some are really stimulated by it; they thrive when there is plenty of variety in their day, and when the unexpected happens. Others are more likely to find any alteration to their accustomed routine both confusing and debilitating. A few mega changes, or a considerable number of minor modifications in any one year, will, generally speaking, lower the stress threshold of most people.

Consider, for example, Peter's situation. It was widely believed that Peter would cope well with the upheaval of all the reorganisation going on at work. He was being moved to an entirely new office block where many of the staff he was going to oversee were unknown to him, but at least his own line manager would remain the same for a time. They were used to working together, and respected each other, which was a considerable help. Meanwhile, Peter and his wife Trudy had just had their third baby; he was considered to be an old hand at fatherhood by now. To meet the needs of their growing family they had decided to move to a larger house before the new baby started walking. Suddenly, though, they found just the right house, put in an offer which was accepted, and everything came together and went through much quicker than expected, so they found themselves moving when the baby was only two weeks old. Then Peter's brother was tragically killed in a road accident, and he was devastated. To crown it all, Trudy had mild but significant post-natal depression.

All these things happening so close together proved too much for Peter. It was not at all surprising that he should begin to show signs of stress. Fortunately, however, with a sympathetic line manager who was able to temporarily reduce his workload, and to extend the deadlines he was up against, Peter was able to pull through.

The vulnerability of an individual to stress will almost certainly be increased when he has to make several adaptations in different areas of his life, at around the same time. When too many changes occur too closely together they can overwhelm a person's usual ability to manage. Although he may well have negotiated each individual event successfully, he is likely to find that even a minor subsequent demand on him becomes just one demand too many; a number of successive changes inevitably has a cumulative effect. It is not the scale of any specific stress so much as the magnitude of the overall load in any one period of time that has to be considered. All this is summed up in Diagram 2.

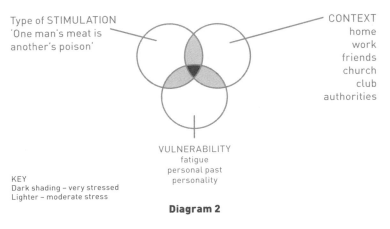

Type of STIMULATION
'One man's meat is another's poison'

CONTEXT
home
work
friends
church
club
authorities

VULNERABILITY
fatigue
personal past
personality

KEY
Dark shading – very stressed
Lighter – moderate stress

Diagram 2

A common complaint today is 'pressure at work', but that is not an entity in itself. It is generally the result of a combination of several widely differing components. A great variety of factors may contribute towards the overall experience of 'pressure'. It is important that any individual tries to be quite specific about which aspects of the working day are contributing to his experience of overall pressure at work, so that he can seek suitable remedies or make his own adjustments.

It may not necessarily be the job itself, but something in the environment, the management structure or personnel issues that are the last straw for an already stressed person. We sometimes forget the subtle effect that climate in general, and heating and ventilation in particular, have on our wellbeing. Like many other factors they will not be the sole cause of stress, but where such conditions are less than optimum they make a significant contribution to discomfort. Other possible culprits to consider are poor lighting, lack of space, incorrectly positioned seating and the prevailing noise level.

These days few, if any, people have the security (and possible tedium) of a job for life, but while they are in employment they do need to be clear about their role within that organisation. Fuzzy lines of communication and overlapping areas of responsibility are significant sources of stress for people. It is very much worse when roles and tasks are not clearly specified, or are changed imperceptibly, so that people do not know what is actually required of them. Sometimes such ambiguities are allowed to continue, either because they have not been recognised before, or no one has been willing to take the initiative and clarify muddy areas. It is important to clarify what precise aspect of the job is proving to be stressful so that the problem can be discussed with the relevant person.

The actual work routine, or lack of it, is another point worthy of attention. Some people work best when they are given clear guidelines so that they know exactly what they are required to do. When they know the standard operating procedures they are happy to work in a steady, orderly way, step by step, keeping to a proven and reliable routine. Other people prefer to have the opportunity of completing their tasks in their own way, with room to introduce an element of variety from time to time. This is necessary for them in order to keep their interest alive and to help them concentrate on the job. The first group of people are likely to find any changes in the work environment, or the practices they have grown used to, quite unsettling. The second group react differently; they welcome the challenges and fresh opportunities that reorganisation offers. We will look at the effect of change, and how to negotiate it to minimise stress, in Chapter 9.

The smooth running of our lives depends upon predictability. Much of what we do on a daily basis is a matter of routine; we don't have to think about having a shower, getting dressed or all the other ordinary activities of life, we just get on and do them. Likewise, many of our initial conversational gambits are equally habitual. We greet someone with the conventional 'How are you?' and do not generally expect to receive a long discourse on their personal triumphs and trials. It is a time-honoured greeting to which the expected response is some acknowledgement of the speaker's presence; neither more nor less. And that is how our lives tick along relatively smoothly – until we are jolted out of the familiar pattern by some uncharacteristic behaviour or response. When a neutral remark provokes an unexpectedly sharp or bitter response it is important to recognise that such a riposte was probably an example of the last-straw syndrome. It is more likely to be evidence of a stressed individual than of personal animosity.

When we ourselves find any such plaintive cry or angry response being, as it were, wrung from us, this must surely be regarded as a clarion call to stop and reflect. We must ask ourselves what might be troubling us behind that polite face we generally present to the world. Fortunately our God knows our background, even when we have forgotten or suppressed all knowledge of it. He knows our reactions and our deepest secrets, and accepts us just the same. He issues a particular invitation to all stressed individuals. He says, 'Come to me, all you who are weary and burdened, and I will give you rest' (Matt. 11:28). This is not the rest of doing nothing, but of working with Him and walking at His pace, which is a very different one from the prevailing twenty-first-century scramble.

Everyone has their breaking point. For some it comes early, with relatively little pressure being put upon them. A few are extraordinarily resilient. They seem to thrive on the stimulation of crises and of constant demands being made upon their energies and resourcefulness. Most of us would place ourselves somewhere on a line between these two opposite ends of a stress-resistance spectrum.

We all need to recognise when we are beginning to be under stress, in order that we may make compensatory adjustments somewhere in our lives. The most effective intervention is likely to be that which is aimed at the stressful situation itself. Remedial action generally needs to be composed of some small, practical and achievable steps. We are much more likely to begin and to continue with a series of small steps than we are to take one giant stride. The aim of these modest measures is to gradually deal with the source, or sources, of stress. We cannot eliminate it altogether, but we can diminish or nullify a number of contributory causes so that we are more able to deal with those stresses that really are inevitable.

When we are going through one of those periods when there is a great deal of unavoidable strain and stress in one area of life, the situation can often be managed indirectly. It is generally possible to make some appropriate modification in another area of our lives. For instance, a busy and demanding time at work can often be managed by lessening, for a while, the number of voluntary duties outside the job itself.

Along with this reduction in activity there also needs to be an increase in relaxation and energy-restoring pursuits in whatever disposable time is left. It is a case of ensuring that when there is extra demand on our personal batteries we make sure that they are regularly topped up. When energy is being depleted in one area of life it must be constantly replenished through another sector.

Sometimes we succumb to stress because our foundations are shaky. Early experiences may have conspired to convince us that people in general are not to be trusted. So we play safe, restrict ourselves and only engage in those aspects of life where we can remain in control at all times. We may have decided that the only way to feel secure is to be self-sufficient. In time, that leads to loneliness and eventual personal bankruptcy. We are made for God, to be in relationship with Him and with His people, rather than for isolation.

We are invited to exchange the insecurity of a life based on the shifting sands of past experiences, for the solid rock of one built upon a relationship with Christ. He invites us to walk in step with Him; in fact, to be yoked to Him. Religion can be a most burdensome thing, particularly when we pick up warped ideas about God (see Chapter 10). However, to be bonded with Christ is freedom. His yoke is easy to wear, because it is tailor-made to fit each individual. In His days as a carpenter He would have made each yoke a perfect fit for each particular ox. The yoke He offers to every person is a perfect fit, just for them.

Sorting the Wheat from the Chaff

Using Diagram 2, decide which stress factors are currently inevitable for you, and which are chaff that you can do something about.

1. Things which stress me and which I can often avoid, or take steps to minimise include _____

_____

2. These things I cannot avoid: _____

_____

Therefore I must not approach them in an exhausted state. I must also endeavour to follow them with a 'recovery period' that recharges my batteries.

3. The sectors (context) where my tolerance of stress is likely to be diminished currently include _____

_____

4. The times and situations when I am personally more vulnerable to stress at the moment include _____

_____

SEARCHING QUESTIONS

1. Is my life built on the shifting sand of past experiences, or on the solid rock who is Christ, the Saviour? Read Matthew 7:23–27.

2. Have I accepted the yoke of Christ? Read Matthew 11:28–30.

3. AT THE SLIPPERY SLOPE

'My daughter says I don't laugh like I used to,' said one man. As he talked it was clear he was weighed down with too many diverse tasks. He was not able to give adequate attention to them all, and he had become unable to decide which ones he either wanted, or most needed, to focus on. The result was he seldom had the gratification of doing a really good job in any one sector, and so he lost out on a major source of satisfaction and reward. Instead of being on top of his job it had begun to get on top of him. It was beginning to dominate his life in a burdensome and unrewarding way. He had lost his sense of humour and his zest for living. In subtle ways his resourcefulness and his resilience were depleted; only little signs, but important ones, and ones that were picked up by those closest to him.

When any aspect of life requires particular effort it is important that this is balanced by an adequate return in the form of fulfilment or gratification either from the work itself or from somewhere else in life. The effort/reward balance needs to be kept about right. Any river that continually flows on without being replenished soon runs dry.

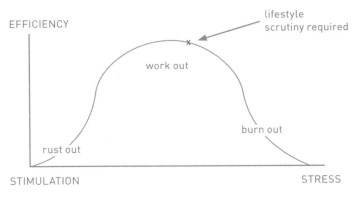

Diagram 3: Productivity Curve

There comes a time in any endeavour when the law of diminishing returns applies (see Diagram 3). At some point any increase in effort is followed by a decrease in productivity. It is at this stage, when over the hill of peak performance and onto the slippery slope towards burn-out, that people need to pause and evaluate their lifestyle. Some adjustments are called for. Everyone has their own bell-shaped curve; for some it is higher or broader, while for others it may be located more to the left of the graph. However, there is a slippery slope waiting for all, and only a balanced lifestyle can prevent the downturn. No one is immune. Anyone who continues without a break, and without making any necessary lifestyle changes, will become increasingly unproductive, and unhappy.

The beginning of the downward slope is the time to take action. At this stage a few adjustments may be enough to keep a person going in near-peak condition. Deciding just what changes would be easiest and quickest to implement, and which would yield the greatest benefit, calls for a personal sort-out as soon as the decline is noticed. This needs to be a wide-ranging survey of every area of life, noticing what is being omitted, or is in very short supply, as well as what is currently burdensome. In the General Confession of the Anglican Church, sins of omission are mentioned before those of commission. It is always wise to look at what we leave out as well as what we put into any situation.

Leslie began to realise how much work was dominating his life. He was even dreaming of work issues, so he decided to take stock. He discussed his workload with his line manager, who was able to encourage him, and to point out some ways he could be more efficient. He began to take a definite lunch break, sometimes swimming, sometimes jogging, and often going out for a meal with colleagues. Seeing what a difference this made to him, his wife suggested they resumed seeing more of friends some weekends. His work did not change, but he was managing to live in a more balanced way.

The purpose of a lifestyle scrutiny is to enable the individual to find out where he can make useful changes. The aim is to assist him in finding options that are likely to be open to him, but of which he was previously unaware. A systematic evaluation of personal, social, spiritual, recreational and work arrangements will generally reveal some areas where fine-tuning can contribute to a reduction in overall stress levels. Small changes in several areas of life are often more beneficial than one mega one, and also more likely to be implemented.

The old adage 'All work and no play makes Jack a dull boy and Jill a dull girl' has perhaps never been more true than it is at the start of the third millennium. Just as an aircraft cannot fly unless the weight that it carries is within its limit, and proper care is also taken to see that it is correctly distributed, so it is with us.

Some people still neglect to take sufficient care of their most fundamental needs. They do not bother to take an adequate and varied diet, while others consistently go short of exercise or sleep. Anyone can compensate for a few broken nights, and some have to adapt to a run of them for a time, but adopting the habit of burning the candle at both ends over a long period is heading for trouble. Those people who keep themselves turbocharged every moment of their day are keeping themselves on high alert all the time. Not surprisingly, they may not then get properly refreshing sleep. They have in effect become addicted to maintaining their own unrelenting level of activity.

Such 'adrenalin junkies' have yet to learn that they are not indispensable and also to appreciate that there really is more to life than increasing its speed. Those are two of the twelve 'Lessons From a Busy Life' that Edward England draws out when reflecting on his heart attack, and which he writes about most movingly in his book *The Addiction of a Busy Life*.[1]

When people are stressed, the effect is generally felt and noticed most in their personal relationships. In families, at work, in the church and wherever people interact with each other, it is true that if one person suffers then all suffer with them. Often there is a gradual withdrawal of real interest and involvement with the affairs of these others, because of the increasing absorption with one's own overriding preoccupations. There is a tendency to neglect social contacts just when companionship and broader horizons are most needed.

All of us need to keep our friendships alive and in good repair, but perhaps never more so than when we are starting to slide down that slippery slope. Quality time with the family must be especially safeguarded. Too often, at times of stress, those nearest to us have to make do with the fag ends of our attention, and even those may be grudgingly given. Sometimes, of course, family affairs are a part of the pressure people are under, and then they especially need the wider horizon of social life. A brief break from it all with congenial companions enables people to return to the fray refreshed and with a better perspective on problems.

People's needs in this respect vary enormously. For some extravert types, association and conversation with others is their very life-blood, but every one of us is created a social being. Even the most introvert people have a need for the amicable company of one or two others who will accept them as they are. When we overlook this elementary human need we impoverish ourselves and become much more susceptible to stress.

Another early casualty to the stress syndrome is the value given to times of recreation. As the pressures of life increase so the time allocated to recreation generally decreases. For a number of workaholics the concept of taking any time off at all is anathema. Recreation is regarded as something merely to pass the time, a diversion that is restricted to those with little else to occupy them. It is seen as a true pastime, rather than an opportunity for recharging essential batteries. For such people recreation tends to be on the very margins of their concerns, a rather despised optional extra.

This attitude is the legacy of a puritanical Protestant work ethic that we will challenge in Chapter 12.

When under stress it is important to consider whether one is using all the possible resources that broadly come into the category of aesthetic and cultural pursuits. We have to pay due regard to those things that nourish and feed us in the very widest sense, as well as those things that are being a drain. Recreational pursuits are not the icing on the cake, to be dismissed with a wry or sarcastic 'Chance would be a fine thing'. They are aspects of our humanity, accomplishments mediated through the right half of the brain, which is a much neglected territory in our left-brain dominated society.

The left brain is active in analysing, measuring, abstracting and doing things in linear sequence. It revels in the precise use of words, numbers and clear diagrams. The right brain deals with things spatially rather than sequentially, with synthesis more than analysis, and it utilises metaphors more than facts.

I sometimes pick up the impression that many stressed-out people consider that our Creator God is only interested in the activity of their left-brain hemisphere, and that He probably regrets making the other half! Neglect of the creative, imaginative and artistic areas of our being means that we begin to resemble those stunted thorn bushes that are so characteristic of desert landscapes. We are unlikely to blossom and bear the fruit expected of trees that are planted by the rich River of Life unless we utilise the whole of our created selves; the right half of our brains as well as the left.

Chronic fatigue means that there is seldom any energy or enthusiasm for this wider, richer life without which our personalities become impoverished. This state can be likened to the subtle effects that a lack of vitamins has on our bodies and minds. When the level is low, but not critically so, we do not cease to function but sooner or later we reach a state of depletion when we no longer live up to our full potential.

What seems to happen once the time of peak performance

has passed is that when someone realises that either the volume or the standard of their work has deteriorated (if only in their own estimation) they redouble their efforts without a break. We have already seen in Chapter 1 how very important it is to pause between bouts of activity, and to punctuate periods of work with interludes that serve as necessary preparation for the next round of action. Instead of following this principle and taking a mini-break to consider why their response has faded, most people at this point redouble their efforts without any pause at all. The result is likely to be even less satisfactory work, so the whole cycle is repeated, still without a restorative break, and stress is the inevitable result, as shown in Diagram 1.

As well as briefly, but regularly, lessening the tension in which we hold our bodies and minds throughout the day it is important to periodically take longer times of recovery. This is the concept of night following day, and of having a weekend break or its equivalent after a week's work. In today's more fitful time schedules any periods of prolonged or unusual activity should ideally be followed by adequate compensatory recovery periods. These do not have to be prolonged spells. They do need to take account of the inevitable toll that travel, sustained concentration, unfamiliar surroundings and a disrupted routine are likely to exact, and we should factor in recovery time after particularly draining activities, so as to avoid longer periods of being too stressed out to function well.

Another problem that often comes to the fore as the slippery slope begins to take its toll is that of perfectionism. The alternative is not to accept sub-standard or slip-shod work, but to settle for doing a job that is good enough to achieve the purpose of the task. We should aim to do a 'good enough' job rather than a flawless one. This is a hard concept for many people to embrace. It generally requires much help from friends and colleagues, and often the assistance of a trained counsellor as well.

No one continues to work well unless they receive an adequate reward for the effort and the time that they put into the job. Despite our get-rich-quick, lottery-obsessed society, money is not the only, or necessarily the best, incentive. As well as providing enough to live on, employment also needs to provide some intangible job satisfaction for each individual. This may be its intellectual challenge, or because it is seen as a necessary stepping-stone on the way to something better. Work that some would regard as routine and dull may provide an agreeable social climate for others. Some types of work meet a person's altruistic or other ideals, or are undertaken to satisfy some particular personal requirement.

Someone once calculated that if we get satisfaction from 70 per cent of our work we can manage the other 30 per cent on the back of that fulfilment. A common finding in stressed individuals is that this ratio is upset, if not actually reversed. Many are expending too much of their time and energy on areas which yield them the least reward, so they are in negative balance.

Sometimes people unwittingly allow themselves to be robbed of their vitality by the constant drain of relentless uncertainty. A judicious question in the right quarter can often resolve the issue. Few things are as draining as never being quite sure how far one is expected to go in a matter, or exactly how much initiative one is permitted to employ. It is important for everyone to know just where the limits of their responsibility really lie, because this sets them free to work right up to their boundaries. When there is ambiguity about the role of an individual, confusion about decision making, or areas of overlapping responsibility, people will become frustrated and their energy will be depleted.

Ill-defined lines of communication are another fertile source of misunderstanding and frustration that slowly sap away at the energy levels of everyone who is affected by the obscurity. When there are several such shadowy areas in a workplace, the effect on individuals is like a chronic, undetected loss of blood. People become energy-anaemic: listless, lethargic and dulled.

When people are stressed they are liable to confuse their role with their selfhood. When their role at work is changed so that their function is now more peripheral, they may regard themselves, their whole self, as being on the sideline. If they see the change as a downgrading in some particular aspect, they are liable to consider that their value as a person has been lowered and they may feel degraded and demeaned. It is easy in the consequent disappointment and upset to mistake role at work for identity as a person. At times like these the corrective balance of a well-rounded lifestyle is especially needed. People must be able to offset reverses in one area with positive, confidence-building relationships and activities elsewhere in their lives, if they are to maintain their equanimity.

Another pressure resulting from reorganisation at work is when a person is given a new area of responsibility and expected to just pick it up or grow into it without specific training. Today there are a multitude of different courses available so there is no need to allow oneself to just muddle along under pressure. Once the needs of the new role have been identified, it is important for individuals to ensure that they have the adequate tools to do the job allocated to them.

Conflicts between colleagues affect the more sensitive and astute people, but leave others unscathed. Some organisations maintain the ethos of sweeping disagreements under the carpet, where they continue to fester and erupt from time to time. Where there are conflicting leadership styles that show themselves in different areas, this can be unsettling, perhaps even the last straw for a vulnerable person. Lower down the hierarchy, and therefore having more impact on the majority of people, is the stress of working in a team where two people are at loggerheads. Perhaps it is even more stressful to work where there is clear but covert dissatisfaction; continual grumbling that rumbles on without ever being brought out into the open and addressed in a straightforward way. Spending hours of your day in a cloud of more or less veiled hostility may make a good TV soap situation but in real life it increases tension, and decreases satisfaction with the job.

Have a Shake-Out, to Avoid Burn-Out

1. **Review your lifestyle**: are your basic needs being met? Consider food, fun, friendship, fellowship, finances and times to put your feet up.
2. **Relationships**: are you keeping them in good shape?
3. **Recreation**: do you regularly listen to music, paint, garden, exercise or do anything to help you unwind? Are you growing spiritually?
4. **Refuel**: do you regularly restock the mental, emotional, cultural, spiritual and relational areas of your life?
5. **Recovery time**: do you take enough mini-breaks during the day, and longer ones after times of greater stress?
6. **Rewards**: how much satisfaction does each area of your work yield? Are you fulfilled through other areas of your life, and in other roles?
7. Do you have the **right tool** for each job that you do?
8. Can you bring yourself to **re-focus** on the 'good enough'?
9. **Reduce uncertainty**: do you ask questions, and check out your assumptions?
10. **Responsibilities**: are your boundaries clear, and your resources adequate?

NOTE

1. Edward England, *The Addiction of a Busy Life* (Crowborough: Aviemore Books, 1998).

4. BAGGAGE FROM THE PAST

Whatever we do, wherever we go, we take our memories with us. Some of these are easily accessible and effortlessly retrieved whenever they are needed. A little more concentration may often be required to bring some others to mind, but nonetheless they can be recalled quite smoothly whenever they are wanted. A whole lot more seem somewhat capricious; they may receive no attention for many years, then suddenly, and seemingly out of the blue, pop back into awareness.

We have a vast memory bank. It is as though there is a section holding those memories that may be required at any time. These are only just out of consciousness, and can be instantly recalled whenever they are needed in daily life. I may not have been thinking about a certain person, but when I meet him or her in the street there is instant recognition. As I stop and speak with the person, more memories come back and I am able to ask about his family and concerns. It just needed a slight trigger to open the door and in came the right memory, suitably on cue. Whatever else may be occupying you at the time, when someone asks you a question you can switch tracks and give an appropriate answer.

There are other memory stores deeper inside. The answers are there, but we have, as it were, to look along the shelves of our memory to find the right one. They do not just come into consciousness on cue, they have to be looked for. Then there are the archives. These are not often required and so are stored in a remote area. They contain the family chronicles, land registers, documents about people, and any number of records about emotive things that happened long ago. All the annals of the past are stored here, for nothing is thrown away.

There are many reasons for needing to refer to these old, forgotten records of past events. The custodian allows access to genuine enquirers who can give satisfactory evidence of identity and of their 'need to know'. Archives may be consulted because it is hoped that they will throw some light on a current difficulty or puzzling situation. Sometimes it is intellectual curiosity, seeking answers to questions that have been around a long time, but never fully pursued.

The custodian has a whole bunch of keys that will gain access to the archives by different routes. Sometimes a specific scent will unleash a string of memories leading to the crucial one. Hearing the snatch of a tune, a particular phrase said in a certain way, catching a distinctive facial expression and many other reminders may also unlock the way to what has been 'forgotten' for many years.

Sometimes there is a 'combination lock' to a memory store. Get all the digits right and the lock swings smoothly open. Miss one out, or get it wrong, and the lock will stay in place until all is clearly right for the store to open. It may be a particular sight with an associated sound in a similar location or under particular weather conditions to the original incident that brings it suddenly, and perhaps unsought, to mind. Memories are sometimes hidden away and out of reach for years, then something happens and back they come with all their original impact. At the age of forty, or whatever the chronological age now reached, the memory may vividly bring back not only the original incident, but also all the four-year-old's feelings too. Whatever it was that happened thirty-six years ago is recalled, along with all the associated feelings of the young child – and they lose nothing of their force in the storage. To re-experience as a four-year-old can seem primitive and illogical to the adult that that child has now become. However sophisticated we may have become, the person you and I are today is influenced by all the things that happened in our earlier years.

As well as being the person we are now, we all have, well hidden inside us, traces of the struggling young adult, the embarrassed older teenager and the awkward younger one. There are memory traces of the carefree (or otherwise) young child, the trying toddler and all the ages we have ever been, right back to our very beginning.

This is an example of the Russian Doll syndrome. Tourists love to bring back those painted wooden mementos. A rotund, smiling woman, usually with a brightly coloured apron and head scarf, can be taken apart in the middle to reveal another, smaller but otherwise identical version inside. In fact there is a succession of ever smaller, but otherwise indistinguishable, dolls inside until you get to the papoose-like finale. This would be a better model for our purposes if the portrayal found in each successive inner layer were to clearly depict different, earlier, ages that the individual has grown through, but it gives the general idea.

Most of the time, all these earlier experiences are out of our awareness. They are safely, and more or less successfully, modified by the adult we have since become. Then, out of the blue, we respond to some cue or other more as the three-, six- or sixteen-year-old we once were than as the adult we now are. Something in the present has awakened the feelings aroused by an experience, or series of experiences, in the past that were not fully processed, integrated and dealt with at the time.

The emotions aroused by an earlier and long forgotten disappointment, rejection, hurt or whatever are often aroused without there being any recall of the incidents that originally provoked them. Only the last straw is experienced. When there is no obvious connection with the preceding bales of straw, as it were, then it is no wonder that the ensuing reaction seems incomprehensible and out of place. When we start dealing with some of these emotions that have become detached from the original provocation it may be the first, rather than the last, straw. We may find ourselves being profitably led back to still other straws that have lain on our backs for some time – or more literally, have been locked up inside ourselves. When we are able to shed some of those early straws, our relationships with others are likely to improve.

It is when we are unable, for whatever reason, to deal with distressing emotional issues at or around the time that they occur that they sink into the memory vault, out of awareness, and get forgotten. Then when something in the present has a resemblance to some part of the unresolved, earlier issue it is as if the adult has trodden on an emotional landmine. The reaction is sudden, forceful and unexpected. Sometimes it is also devastating. As a friend of mine put it, we can seldom escape from the unpaid emotional debts of earlier years.

Many people find it helpful to picture their lives as a house. The middle floors are the living areas, where all the ordinary activities of life take place, and where we feel most at home. It is the area of our lives where we are most conscious of our thoughts, feelings, reactions and our general behaviour. But some of our activity, and our inner reactions and feelings, have become automatic over the years. We are no longer conscious of why we do or do not do certain things, or what makes us respond repeatedly in the way that we do.

We often have to admit that we are not fully masters in our own house. We are not as free as we would like to be. This is because upstairs in the attic there are 'parental residues'. These contain all those messages we received as we grew up, and which we have carefully stored away. They consist of both loving, nurturing memories, and prohibitive, punitive ones, so they are generally a very mixed bag. These messages come mainly from our parents, but also from other authority figures and the various role models we adopted from time to time.

Hopefully most of these 'parental' messages are positive and nurturing. When this is so, the adult in the living areas can call upon the wisdom of the 'parents' in his own attic. Much of this has become automatic. There are all those life-preserving messages like 'Look both ways before crossing the road' and 'Don't play with matches', which are internalised, and become part of the way we live.

Up here are stored away memories of all those occasions when the person knew himself to be loved and wanted, an acceptable and worthwhile person. They also include the beneficial aspects of his moral and religious upbringing. These are messages that can be reactivated in a very constructive and helpful way whenever the person needs support and encouragement. All this is available for the adult, in the living room of his house, to call upon when the need arises.

But few, if any, people have such an idyllic background that there are only positive, sustaining and growth-enhancing messages stored in the attic. There are also all those 'shoulds' and 'oughts' that haunt us; the long list of things that we 'must' and 'mustn't' do. There are also residues of disharmony and disappointment, and sometimes of absent, angry or even antagonistic 'parent' perceptions. All those school reports that said 'Could do better' and were reinforced by obvious parental regret, even outright dissatisfaction, leave their legacy in the attic.

Very often the child inside the adult remains more or less dissatisfied with himself without necessarily knowing why. Even though most of us forget a large part of what is stored in the attic, it still exerts an influence whenever something sets off the alarm. Children who have been continually subject to unyielding, rigid standards are likely to become prey to irrational guilt that they have not done things exactly right. They can never quite satisfy the voice in the attic that calls for perfection.

It is almost as though we have an automatic tape recorder hidden in our attic. At certain cues it will softly but relentlessly play back the response that has been internalised and keyed in over the years. We need to track these down one by one, and replace each tape with our own updated response.

Children who have repeatedly been shamed and shown that they cannot do things satisfactorily are likely to have the automatic tape 'You can't do it'. When adults realise they are responding to such a tape they can make a conscious decision to replace it with 'I can do it', and act on that assumption. At first this new behaviour may be accompanied by any number of uncomfortable feelings. Whenever they asserted themselves as children they may have suffered distressing, even dire, consequences. When they begin to assert themselves as adults the same feelings of dread may initially occur as automatically as the inner verbal message. The more often they consciously change the 'I can't' to 'I can', and proceed to act accordingly, the sooner the negative thoughts, and the accompanying feelings, will begin to lose their force. Gradually the positive message they are now giving themselves will take over from the old recorded one.

Many of us have a large library of tapes in our attic, most of which are by now out of date and need to be re-recorded. Until the time comes when they are erased, or better still recorded over with a positive message, they will continue to whisper their old message right on cue. Recently I was listening to a woman who drove herself to meet the needs of others so that she had little time or energy to look after any but the most immediate of her own needs. Lucy used to enjoy all sport and physical activity but now seldom found, or made, the opportunity to fit any into her demanding schedule. Long, vigorous bike rides had once refreshed her, and we discussed how she could fit in some cycling. Working from home, and with open heathland nearby, she said, 'I could go for a ride at lunch time, then have a quick bath', with the clear implication that she should not spend more time and attention on herself. Whenever 'shoulds' and 'oughts' appear they are generally from the attic, and need to be examined afresh to see if they are still applicable today. I asked her whether she would be able to change this to 'I'll go for a ride then have a nice bath'. The small change from 'quick' to 'nice' would be a clear message to herself that she is worthy of this much attention and little bit of luxury. She needed to affirm herself by giving herself just a little more time and enjoyment. Simply changing one word helped her to begin to change her attitude to herself. When this improved she was able to make more small but significant changes in her daily routine. Each one was only a small change, but added together they were enough to reduce the stress she was putting on herself.

It seems to me to be significant that when a blind man was taken to Jesus in the village of Bethsaida (Mark 8:22), Jesus did not perform an instantaneous healing. He first led the man out of the village, and away from all the gossip and chatter. He took him out of earshot of those who, with the belief system of the time, would be telling him that his blindness was a punishment for his own shortcomings. Once outside the village Jesus touched the eyes of the blind man, who was very honest. Initially his sight was only partially restored, and he said so. Another touch, and then he really could see everything clearly.

There are times when we need to go out of the village, away from all those out-of-date accusatory voices coming from our personal 'attic'. And then we also need to persist with the remedial action. Healing and restoration generally take time, co-operation, trust and effort.

So the attic tends to contain a varying mix of constructive and useful themes interspersed with ones that are intractably restrictive and obstructive. When these troublesome ones are roused it can indeed be the last straw. We need to be vigilant at noticing, naming and negativing these straws; for two negatives *do* make a positive. Sometimes we need to convince ourselves 'I am not "no good" at it', and this will enable us to realise there is no reason why we cannot do it. Then we can act on the positive outcome 'Of course I can do it'.

When there are good relationships in the living area these attic remnants can often be detected, discussed and brought out into the open. For some people talking things over with trusted and wise friends may be sufficient to loosen their grip, but for others some professional counselling may be called for.

Christians who begin to examine the noxious influences coming from their attic area may run into a particular difficulty. Often our concept of the Heavenly Father is unconsciously contaminated with unhelpful distortions based on unfortunate early experiences. When this has happened, pastoral support is more vital than ever while the individual works through their dilemma. More will be said about this in Chapter 10.

As well as taking into ourselves attitudes that originated from outside, we may also employ a reverse psychological process. Instead of taking something from outside and introjecting it, that is to say making it a part of our own beliefs about ourselves, we also do the opposite. We project onto someone else many of our own characteristics and impulses, generally those that we do not like. When they threaten our self-esteem we throw them out onto someone or something else because it seems to be easier to deal with an external threat. We are all prone to label as 'unfair' or 'biased' an exam or a selection process that we fail to pass. It is often a case of an unskilled workman blaming his tools for his unsatisfactory performance.

When we dislike something about ourselves we are likely to try and deal with it by denying that it is in fact our own baggage. We feel so much better when we can hand it over to someone else to carry for us. We need to identify such baggage as our property, reclaim it from the carousel of life's journey, and deal with it in a more conscious and adult way. Unclaimed projections interfere with relationships in every area of life.

I once found myself being increasingly irritated by a senior colleague. He was an affable, hardworking Mr Nice Guy and I could not understand my growing frustration. He sometimes took decisions and forgot to inform me. He would float a bright idea and then leave another (me!) to do it all. Being involved with so many things he was inclined to rush in late, and dash out early. No wonder I found these things trying, because they are my own traits too.

As well as an attic our house also has a cellar. This is where all that is both childish and childlike can be found. Every now and then the creative child comes up into the living area and persuades the adult to play, to laugh and have fun, to loosen up a bit. And Jesus commanded us to be like children; like the trusting, playful, joyous, humble child (Matt. 18:3). We need to widen the access from cellar to living area so our creative child can come and go more freely.

Sometimes the door between cellar and living area has become locked, and it may even be that the key is thrown away because of all the other troublesome, quarrelling children who are there. Here languishes the clamouring child, the one whose wants and needs were seldom met and so he does not know what it is to trust anyone. Here cowers the cringing child, the one who was rebuffed and hurt in many ways and has come to believe that no one loves him. Sometimes the experiences that have consigned this child to the cellar have even convinced him that he is himself unloveable.

When the presence of these children in the cellar is recognised, the adult in the living area probably needs to find a wise and trusted friend to accompany him down into the cellar to rescue them one by one. Sometimes they may be in need of 'hospital care' when skilled counselling is called for, together with the 'nursing' that a vibrant Christian fellowship can provide. Always they will need the healing touch of the suffering, risen and triumphant Lord Jesus. While He was on earth He sometimes dealt one to one with people. At other times He addressed individual needs within the crowds that gathered to hear Him, which is one reason why we should never give up on public worship with others. Jesus said, 'Let the little children come to me, and do not hinder them ...' (Matt. 19:14).

Sometimes relationships with others go wrong because people call to one another from attic to cellar, or cellar to attic, instead of staying in their respective living rooms. The adult has temporarily been taken over by the internalised parent or young child. The relationship between two adults in the present is being hampered by the baggage each of them carries from their past. The 'critical parent' in one may evoke the guilty or frightened 'child' inside the other person, and they react to each other from these psychological positions.

I remember voicing my concern for both my own parents when my mother's Alzheimer's disease worsened. That was an 'adult' statement. A respected older woman immediately said, 'Of course you'll give up your job and go down to look after her.' This was a 'parental' comment which almost tipped me into both a timid and an angry 'child' state. It was authoritarian, the speaker assuming she knew what would be the right thing to do, without knowing the circumstances. Fortunately, I was able to weigh up the situation, talk it through with good friends, and come to an adult decision. For me to have reacted from a 'child' position to such a dictatorial directive would not have helped me or my parents. It made me be more careful what I chose to share in front of that woman.

The 'helpless child' aspect of one person sometimes calls forth the nurturing parent side of another, which may be helpful in a crisis. But the same helpless stance may also activate the 'critical parent' in another person, and then that relationship is unlikely to be a happy one. Mutually enriching relationships require that all parties are functioning through their adult 'living rooms', with little interference from either the 'attic' or the 'cellar'.

Baggage Tags

1. There is much wisdom up there in the attic. Be sure to use it.

2. There is also a lot of lumber. Give yourself time to 'go outside the village' with the Lord, and sort through it.

3. Examine 'should', 'ought' and 'must' whenever they occur in your conversation, or thoughts. Do they really hold today? Do you choose to continue to live by them?

4. Identify your own persistent internally recorded tapes.
   - Negative the negative to pave the way for a positive.
   - Replace negative tapes with positive ones. You may need help with this.

   To find a list of accredited counsellors you could visit the following websites: www.bacp.co.uk (the British Association of Counselling and Psychotherapy) and www.acc.uk.org (the Association of Christian Counsellors). Alternatively your local library may have a list of counsellors accredited by these two associations.

5. Identify and own your projections. Recognise when you are attributing to someone or something outside you your own failings or prejudices, and even your gifts.

6. Unpaid emotional debts from earlier years often continue to drain current resources. Try to identify and deal with any that remain.

7. If you recognise a 'critical parent' or 'hurting child' in yourself, take that part of you to the great Healer. Jesus never rejects anyone who seeks Him.

5. SAYING YES INSTEAD OF NO

Children learn to say 'No' very early in their speech development. In fact, many children go through a phase when their parents consider that for a time their offspring seem to say little else. Fortunately that stage does pass. Unfortunately though, by the time those children are adults a considerable number of them will find themselves saying 'Yes' when in their heart of hearts they really want to say 'No'.

John was average at school. He did not shine at any lesson or sport; he was neither a duffer nor a joker. He had no outstanding characteristics at all. He had his likes and dislikes, of course, but he generally went along with the suggestions of others in order to feel accepted and wanted. He would say 'Yes' to swimming with his mates when he would have preferred for them all to mess about on their bikes. When he left school he still went along with the suggestions of anyone who was more outgoing, more decisive or who seemed stronger than he felt. And he usually said 'Yes' to any request from someone senior to himself.

This habitual reaction can stem from a number of early influences. Superimposed on these there are likely to be a variety of unmet and often unrecognised needs and frequently some unresolved inner tensions. Loud voices coming from the 'attic' of their being (see Chapter 4 for this analogy) maintain the assumption that it is necessarily wrong to say 'No'. Disobeying those internalised messages generally causes considerable discomfort. Many people prefer to continue living according to the dictates of those out-of-date messages long after they have physically left home, rather than put up with the discomfort of evaluating and updating them. Indeed their influence may be so strong that the very idea of examining their continued relevance to life today does not seem to be an option. It is certainly not an easy one.

Some of the impetus to say 'Yes' when it would be much more

appropriate and sensible to say 'No' also comes from the 'children' down in the 'cellar' of our being (again, see Chapter 4 for this analogy). Rather than live with constant disapproval from significant adults, many people have learned in childhood to suppress their likes and dislikes, and they continue to do so into adult life. In childhood they disowned their own needs, in order to be accepted within the family, and they continue to disregard them in order to be valued, wanted and accepted by their peers.

Such people tend to have grown up with a real need to please those on whom their emotional and physical welfare really did depend at that time. The feelings and the compliance are continued long after they have served their survival value. The adult then reaps the legacy of being virtually unable to displease anyone, however inappropriate acquiescence may actually be. Such people lack a sense of their own intrinsic self-worth.

Saying 'Yes' in words or behaviour had become second nature to John. Because he was interested in several potential offshoots of his main work he agreed to take on the additional responsibility of exploring how two of them could be developed. Whenever someone asked how one or other of them was going, he felt a bit guilty at his lack of progress. He would then let other things slide a bit in order to make some headway, but he had to keep leaving the development aspect to attend to his routine work. He was surrounded by unfinished tasks. There were mounds of journals waiting to be read, so he stopped opening them; and as the plastic-wrapped heaps grew, so did his stress. Despite all the things he was juggling with, he even said 'Yes' when asked to attend a distant conference, but the strain was too much. Fortunately he sought help, and in time he learned to say 'No', 'Not yet', or 'Not this year' when necessary. To his amazement he found he gained the respect of others when he stopped being so automatically acquiescent, and his own self-esteem grew.

A number of sensitive people are afraid to assert themselves and say 'No' because of what they imagine their 'no' may do to the other person. If they themselves have ever, perhaps just once, felt rejected or been hurt in any way at having a request refused they become apprehensive that they will cause similar offence to another. A desire to avoid suffering, for themselves and others, is what compels them to say 'Yes' instead of 'No'. Not wanting to cause suffering to others is, of course, a laudable desire, but applied in this way it overlooks the real damage it causes to the person saying a placatory 'Yes'. People who do so have yet to learn that they are not responsible for the reaction of the other person, only for their own responses and behaviour.

Fear is a powerful motivator. For some it is less unpleasant to suffer the consequences of agreeing to something that they would really prefer to refuse, than it is to face any disagreement. The risk of any possible confrontation often seems too great. 'Peace at any price' does indeed come at a price, the price of personal integrity and wellbeing.

Individuals who are unable to say 'No' when it is reasonable and right for them to do so, put themselves at the beck and call of other people. They are very likely to find themselves being manipulated by others. The subsequent feelings of helplessness when they realise it has happened yet again are all too liable to reinforce their lack of self-esteem. But the cycle can be broken. It won't be done overnight, but it can be done with a little application. The help of supportive and understanding friends will be a great asset in continuing the process of saying 'No' when, all in all, that is the sensible thing to say.

Learning to say 'No' when it is appropriate and right to do so requires that you really are prepared to take charge of your own life. It is for you to decide, under God, how you will apportion your time, your energy, your money and your affections. No one else has the right to do so, although there are always some who will assume that they know better than you what you should be doing. No one else has the right to give advice, unless you ask them to. When you do ask, you need to remind yourself that the opinion given is an option for you to consider, not a command to be obeyed.

Anyone who is beginning to deal with the messages from their 'attic' may need to remind themselves that they are choosing to be the 'actor' in the drama of their own life. They will need to tell themselves that they are no longer prepared to be a reactor to the whims and wishes of other people. They are no longer going to live like a puppet, manipulated by strings that are pulled by someone else.

Some years ago a large and colourful notice on the door of an office caught my attention. It boldly proclaimed 'Please note. Your lack of planning does not constitute my emergency' and went on to give various humorous examples of requests that would not be met. Some people find it very hard to define and stay within their own boundaries. They are inclined to rush into rescuing the improvident, without considering the implications on other claims to their time, energy and attention.

Learning to say 'No' to another person will depend on the ability to say 'Yes' to oneself. Many people cannot apply to themselves the words of the TV advertisement 'Because I'm worth it'.

If you find it hard to say 'No' to a request, try reminding yourself that you are rejecting the appeal, and not the person. This may sound too simple, but many people fail to make the distinction, and fail to say 'No' because they muddle the person with the plea that the person is making.

There are, of course, ways of refusing an inopportune or inappropriate request, without actually using that rather harsh-sounding (to some ears) two-letter word 'No'. Containing the refusal within a whole sentence is clear, direct, unambiguous and should not lead to loss of friendship. Try something like, 'I'm sorry, I'm not available that afternoon.'

If you really would like to help the other person, and are not being manipulated or feeling driven, you might like to offer an alternative. 'I'm sorry I can't manage Tuesday, but would Thursday be any help to you?', or 'I can't do this week at all, would some time next week, say Wednesday, be any use to you?' By naming the alternative that is suitable for you, you are managing to avoid the possibility of having to refuse a second suggestion from the other person. It is important to keep the initiative in your own hands.

If, from your perspective, a persistent request seems unreasonable it may help you to stand your ground by acknowledging the need of the other person. Something like 'I can see your difficulty, but I am afraid that I am unable to help you', could be said confidently and, if required, repeatedly. If it is necessary to repeat the refusal it is most important to stand your ground, and to stick to the same form of words. Just repeat your answer, without any elaboration or explanation. It is not necessary, indeed it is generally unwise, to offer any elucidation. Watch for the other person shifting the grounds for their appeal to you, and stick to your original answer.

You do not have to give a reason, much less an excuse, for refusing a request but it may underline your refusal if you choose to do so. Some possible examples are: 'I'm sorry but my diary is already full for that month/quarter', 'I'm away on holiday/out of the country that week', 'Thank you for asking me, but it is definitely not my calling/gift/thing'. This type of answer should give the right message loud and clear.

A friend of mine tells the story of seeing a woman at a railway station buffet one cold morning. She asked for a cup of hot tea and was pointed to one already poured, waiting on the counter. She said quietly, 'No, I want hot tea, please.' Again the person behind the counter just pointed at the cup on the shelf. This scenario was repeated a couple of times, and other customers began to gather behind the woman. Their impatience was not her responsibility, and finally she managed to get what she was going to pay for, a freshly poured cup of hot tea.

Knowing my tendency to avoid any possible unpleasantness I suspect that I would probably have taken the line of least resistance. If I had picked up the cup of tea that was cooling on the counter I would in fact have been defrauding myself, accepting second best and would no doubt also be feeling somewhat resentful into the bargain. On a cold winter's day, on top of the other discomforts of travel, such an incident might well have been the last straw; a straw that could relatively easily have been avoided by saying 'No'.

We can learn a number of useful lessons from this brief illustration. Notice how the woman stood her ground and kept her cool. She stated her request simply and clearly, and did not alter it. She did not argue, protest or enter into any discussion with the person behind the counter. She just stood patiently where she was and repeated her original request without any elaboration. Her attitude was one of expecting to get what she was asking for, and which the buffet attendant could reasonably be expected to provide. She had no intention of being palmed off with something inferior. She did not allow herself to get angry at the offhand manner of the attendant who was, or in this case was not, serving. She did not allow herself to be rushed, or to feel guilty at standing her ground. She was not manipulated by the silent implication that she 'should' take what was offered, rather than what she was quite reasonably asking for. She firmly kept to her original request, and I imagine that she used a neutral tone in order to keep the emotional temperature even. She did not let herself become anxious because other customers were getting impatient. She recognised that their feelings and how they chose to handle them were their responsibility, not hers. She had successfully resisted falling into the compassion trap.

This occurs when we give a higher priority to what we imagine the other person might be feeling than we do to our own situation. It is a trap because it is our imagination of what might be going on for, and in, someone else and there is no attempt to check out the reality of what is actually going on for the other person.

I often allow myself to feel rushed by the presence of other customers behind me when I am getting books for the church bookstall. It is a time-consuming business entering them through the till, and often I have several other transactions to complete as well. Last time I was there I turned to the customer behind me who had only one card in her hand, and asked if she would like to go next, which she gratefully did.

Then another customer came up before I could resume my business and there was a momentary battle within me as to whether to let her go through too, or to continue with my list. If I had proceeded without first checking whether the next person had a single item or multiple transaction to complete I would have felt uncomfortable at keeping her waiting for so long. So I did check. She too had a number of things to attend to, and I was able to proceed without any hindrance from old 'attic' messages saying that it is 'always' wrong to keep people waiting.

There are a number of other ploys people might use to try and get us to say 'Yes' when they fear we might be going to refuse their request. One is flattery. 'You're so good at it, and I know I can always count on you.' That is in fact a double dose. It is both flattery and manipulation, with the implication that it is your responsibility not to let the side down.

Another manipulative ploy is to favourably compare the person being asked with someone else. 'Last time Jo Bloggs did it, and you know what a disaster that was.' Again, there are hidden implications here that, of course, the recipient of this information will not let the side down and, of course, they can be relied on to do a much better job. Quite possibly they can, but that is not necessarily a valid reason why they should do so on this occasion.

Still another ruse is to shift the ground for the request, perhaps adding a number of special reasons to try and sway the answer towards an affirmative. When the sensible thing is to decline the request, always watch for the other person shifting their position in an effort to get you to change yours. It is sometimes hard not to get sidetracked into other issues, so that you lose sight of your original intention.

I have heard the claim that it is actually 'unchristian' to say 'No'. We are certainly called to go the second mile. That, however, is not the same thing as being a doormat, always there for the express purpose of letting people walk over you. Jesus Christ was filled with compassion for anyone in need. There are many stories in the Gospels of Him healing the sick, but there are also occasions when He moved on, leaving needs unmet.

When His friend Simon sought Jesus out to tell Him that everyone was looking for Him He replied, 'Let us go somewhere else – to the nearby villages – so that I can preach there also. That is why I have come' (Mark 1:38). He did not let the good that He could do deflect Him from accomplishing a better thing, that of getting on with His main task. He had not actually said 'No', but had countered the call to go back and meet all the people who were looking for Him with another plan, one that was in keeping with His primary task.

Then there was the occasion when the disciples of Jesus asked Him to send the crowds away so that they could find themselves something to eat. He effectively said, 'No, you feed them', and when they had foraged around and given Him what little they could muster, He multiplied it many times. Jesus then had the disciples distribute the loaves and fishes, and that evening 5,000 were fed out there in a remote place. But to do that Jesus had to first say 'No' to the initial request.

There is also on record the famous time when Martha and Mary sent an urgent message to Jesus, to tell Him that their brother Lazarus was very sick, and yet Jesus did not obey the summons immediately. Two days later when He did suggest setting out, His disciples, who had not yet heard that news, tried to dissuade Him because of previous death threats, and He had to overrule them (John 11:1–11). It is often not only a question of doing the right thing, but also of choosing the right time to do it.

On one occasion, after a most spectacular deliverance, the man who had been healed begged to go along with Jesus, but this request was refused. We are told that Jesus sent him away, saying, 'Go home to your family and tell them how much the Lord has done for you …' (Mark 5:18–19). No doubt it was flattering to be asked, and to have such a willing follower, but that too did not serve the main purpose of His life.

Break the Habit

1. Develop your 'won't' power, as well as your 'will' power.

2. Be the actor in your life, not a reactor.

3. Remember you are refusing a request, not rejecting the person who makes that request.

4. Beware the compassion trap. Other people's lack of planning does not have to be your emergency! You do not have to rescue everyone.

5. Wrap your 'No' in a single sentence. Be clear and concise: 'I'm sorry I'm not available that afternoon.' If you really do want to help out, offer an alternative of your choice. Keep the initiative for this in your hands: 'I can't do Tuesday, but would Thursday be any use to you?'

6. If the person starts pleading, stand your ground, keep cool and use a neutral tone whilst acknowledging their problem. Remind yourself that it is their problem, not yours: 'I can see your difficulty but I cannot help you out.'

7. Beware flattery: 'I know you won't let us down'; 'You're always so good at these things' and so on.

8. Do not get side-tracked onto other issues. Firmly repeat your refusal using the same form of words.

9. You are not a puppet on a string. You are in charge, under God, of your time, energy and other resources.

10. You are not a doormat.

11. Jesus knew when, and how, to say 'No'. He was always full of compassion, but He did not always say 'Yes'.

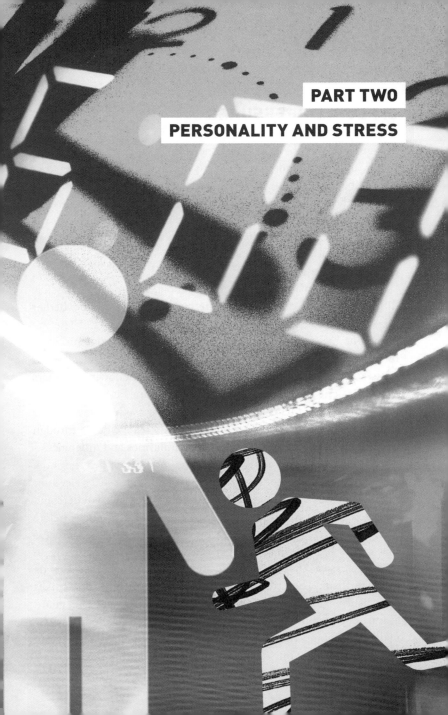

PART TWO

PERSONALITY AND STRESS

6. PEOPLE PRESSURES

'His attitude was the last straw,' one woman stormed as she let off steam after a difficult day. Perfectly normal differences between people of contrasting personalities can become like sandpaper between them unless those differences are understood and respected. Even people with exactly the same personality types are never clones of each other. They merely share certain broad characteristics in common. That cluster of characteristics is sufficient to distinguish them from other groups.

There are many ways to group people, and to study possible differences in personality. There are humorous ones, like whether they are squeezers or rollers of their toothpaste tubes. There are numerous magazine fillers, most commonly by the zodiac sign of birth date. And there are a large number of psychologically and statistically based systems. In this and the three following chapters I have chosen to use the earlier work of Carl Jung, as made popular and accessible by Myers and Briggs.[1] Many people have found their systematised approach to be a practical and creative guide through the enigma of perfectly normal human similarities and differences.

When two or more extraverts (the more there are the more they like it) get together they will appreciate each other's need for interaction and instant feedback. They will perfectly well understand the need to talk things through, exploring various avenues before (eventually) stating their position on the matter. This is a process that others find thoroughly bewildering. As they are naturally so very expressive, there is unlikely to be much of a hidden agenda between them. They share their thoughts and feelings, their likes and dislikes. So much so that at times they may need to guard against doing all the talking, and little of the listening. Some may be in danger of competing with each other for the limelight. Others run the risk of entering into a power struggle with one another.

Two or three introverts[2] (they usually prefer to interact in small numbers) are generally quite content when their conversation contains frequent pauses for silent reflection. They understand and respect each other's need to think things through inwardly, and are happy to allow due time for interior processing before expecting an answer. They are seldom people to give an instant response, their unuttered plea being, 'How can I possibly speak out until I've had time to consider the matter?' This is in marked contrast to the extraverts who operate on the principle that they cannot possibly know their opinion until they (and preferably someone else as well) have heard themselves speak about the subject.

Sometimes introverts are so at home in their own inner world that they forget to speak out the final result of their reflections. This tendency is a cause for much misunderstanding. 'But I told you' – 'No, you never' – 'Well I meant to' is a scenario that has a hundred guises wherever people interact with each other. Introverts in particular are prone to labour on under misconceptions unless they remind themselves to check out their perceptions, which may not always be right. They must remember that people who act on what they assume, without checking things out, are liable to 'make an *ass* of *u* and *me*'.

As they are very different from each other, people with these contrasting values and social needs have much to give to one another. However, those same valuable differences are also a fertile source of tension between them. Because extraverts are so active, and generally gregarious, there is frequently a buzz of energy wherever they congregate. They commonly generate an air of excitement in any team, family or group of friends, and they are likely to bring with them a breadth and freshness of outlook. The downside of this almost whirlwind approach to life is that they can easily overwhelm those of opposite characteristics, who are sometimes rendered deaf to what the extraverts are saying because they say so much, so forcibly and in such a short space of time. As one person described the experience, 'It's like standing under Niagara Falls. I feel as if I will drown if I don't get out and find some dry land quickly.'

Extraverts have a real need for fairly frequent interaction with people (and it really is a need, not an optional extra). Engaging in action, and especially interaction with others, is how they keep their energy levels up and their enthusiasm alive. Even a shy extravert likes to recharge his batteries where there is the buzz of people interacting with each other. Being shy, he may not be the life and soul of the gathering, but he will want to be there. His shyness comes from some particular personal experiences and does not negate his need to regain his energy by being with people.

Just as interaction with others is a necessity for extraverts, so interludes of privacy, and time for reflection, are fundamental requisites for introverts; they are not optional extras. In maintaining their own energy level, extraverts may unwittingly diminish that of introverts who are likely to find interruptions especially trying. Extraverts can actually be a drain on introverts. They are prone to interrupt others in order to pep themselves up, not realising that they are having precisely the opposite effect on the introvert every time they butt in.

People have widely different interpretations of the very same behaviour. For example, when introverts shut the door of their room, be it office, study or den, they are doing so in order to shut themselves in for a while. However this action may well be misconstrued by extraverts, who from their point of view see themselves as being shut out and denied the companionship for which they long. As Robert Burns wrote in his poem 'To a Louse, on seeing one on a Lady's Bonnet at Church':

> **O wad some Pow'r the giftie gie us**
> **To see oursels as eithers see us!**
> **It wad frae monie a blunder free us**
> **An' foolish notion!**

This could be interpreted as 'If one could see oneself as others do, then one would realise one's faults, and be freed of many blunders'.

These different needs are not absolutes, but relative to the overall demands on a person at any one time. An introvert executive kept his office door open whenever he could in the mornings, in order to be available to his staff, so he looked forward to lunching quietly, alone if possible. His deputy, also an introvert, was primarily engaged with figures on his computer most mornings, so by lunchtime he was generally ready for some companionship, and looked to his senior to provide this. Although they were both introverts, their lunchtime needs were frequently different, but being introverts they did not verbalise this, and began to resent each other.

Most people manage to find their own solutions to such dilemmas, but sometimes open-plan offices and living areas can pose quite a problem. Work requirements and other things being equal, it is best all round if the gregarious types, who really are energised by interruptions, can have their desks next to the gangway or coffee point. The more retiring ones will do their best work when they can be found a somewhat more secluded spot, or can surround themselves with files and potted plants to give at least the illusion of privacy.

Another set of contrasting and complementary characteristics is between factual and intuitive types. Factual people tend to focus on the present moment, the known and tangible. They like things to be clear cut and obviously workable. Intuitive people tend to be more interested in the possibilities than the actualities of a situation. They thrive on variety, and respond with bursts of energy when something captures their imagination.

These two groups of people are by nature so different that they are likely to rub each other up the wrong way unless they learn to understand and appreciate one another. If they don't, the disparities in outlook and practice will be a continual irritant between them.

Factual people read the relevant instructions before they commence any task, then begin at the beginning, taking one step at a time without any omissions. They work through an assignment or household chore at a steady pace, in a reliable and consistent manner, and tend to dislike any disruption to their routine. Intuitive people on the other hand are easily bored and tend to welcome the challenge and variety that even minor changes in routine may bring. They would rather experiment than read the instructions and are likely to plunge in at stage two or three rather than the beginning, because they are quick to make connections and see what is needed. They may miss out a phase or two along the way, and still get things done, although occasionally there are glitches that may require the help of their more meticulous friends.

A team or family composed only of factual people will seldom get caught out on detail. They read the small print and need to guard against getting bogged down with minutiae. They may be in danger of having insufficient initiative to amend outworn practices. Any group consisting entirely of intuitive types will have a plethora of bright ideas, but may be deficient in the stickability required to complete tasks once the initial attraction wanes. People with pronounced characteristics in these two categories are both a corrective for and an irritant to each other. At times of stress the vexation they unwittingly cause each other can indeed be the last straw.

One new executive realised he was getting a name for changing his mind, but that was not his intention at all. On every visit to each of his sections he aimed to encourage the staff, but soon found he was actually bewildering them. Each new idea he introduced was meant to build on the one before. He had taken it for granted that they had already grasped and implemented the previous ones he had laid before them. The pace of change he was trying to inaugurate was just too fast. When he realised what was actually happening he slowed down, and took care to clearly spell out his vision in more detail. The workforce were then able to grasp where he wanted to lead the organisation, and to see the implications for themselves, sector by sector, and as individuals. When he allowed people time to adjust to each initiative, before introducing his next objective, the whole operation went more smoothly.

Another fertile source of people misreading each other is the different value systems they operate from. We could reasonably call them the 'head' and the 'heart' people.

Analytical, or 'head' people, weigh things up in terms of underlying principles. They tend to use their heads more than their hearts, and as a result they are able to be objective and detached. These people view matters dispassionately and impersonally, with a tendency to see things in rather black-and-white terms, as either right or wrong. They believe in absolute, impartial justice, and value efficiency very highly. They are task-oriented, tending to drive themselves and others. In their drivenness, and in order to complete projects on time, they sometimes overlook the greater wellbeing of people. If they are both extravert and intuitive, as well as being of an analytical disposition, they may be able to pick up the vibes of discomfort and modify their demands a little. If, on the other hand, they are more factual than intuitive, as well as being analytical, and are also so introverted that they are not in touch with the pockets of discontent around them, they may press on regardless, but be unable to carry others with them.

'Head' people are often poles apart in their understanding and their behaviour from those who are heart- or people-oriented. These are the ones who tend to see issues from the inside, becoming participants in an issue, and in danger of taking sides. They bring to any discussion an insistence that the human element is fully considered, and want plans adapted to the needs of the people who will have to carry them out. They are more likely to see things in shades of grey than in stark black and white, and they believe that mitigating circumstances should temper justice. Such people are inclined to wrap up difficult messages about conduct or productivity in words of encouragement and personal appreciation. These will be treasured by those of similar disposition, but are not recognised as at all meaningful by the 'head' brigade, who see no need to wrap up unpalatable words. 'Heart' people want everyone around them to get along in good harmony with each other at all times. That is their bottom line. They are peace-lovers who tend to be conciliatory in their approach, believing that tact is paramount. They would rather a job was a little late in completion so long as the people working on it can do so amicably.

It is not difficult to see how much these two types need the corrective viewpoint and skills of each other, and yet how very easy it is for them to clash. What the analysts call 'a good discussion' may be perceived as a 'fierce argument', and an uncomfortable one at that, by 'heart' people. When analysts think they are negotiating, others often feel that they are in fact fighting with them. The reconciliatory skills and awareness of emotive issues that characterise 'heart' people can in turn be seen as short-sighted, inconsistent compromise by those who see the world from the other viewpoint.

Analytical people tend to state their position briefly and bluntly, and often come across as confrontational in their manner. This is not appreciated by 'heart' people, who are more concerned with points of agreement than matters of what they see as 'cold' principle. Not surprisingly they themselves tend to come across as somewhat biased.

Working with groups of both types, and getting them to say how they really see their opposites, is always an interesting and illuminating exercise. Here are some other adjectives I have heard applied to the 'heart' people: soft, irrational, unstable, unreliable, irresponsible, inconsistent, naive, imprecise, erratic, short-sighted, doormats, inefficient, cowardly and exasperating.

When it is their turn to express how they feel, in their heart of hearts, when they are with others of like mind who will understand their point of view, here are some of the adjectives 'heart' people use about analysts: tactless, cold, hurtful, unfeeling, uncaring, tunnel-visioned, cruel, dogmatic, superior, pious, legalistic, bombastic, callous brutes and slave drivers.

If there is time to work with them for long enough, someone from each 'side' will eventually call out 'unchristian' and it is not hard to see why. One group exalts Truth and Justice while the other puts greater store on Peace and Harmony. All of these are Christian values and need to be viewed together, rather than being seen in isolation, and as if they are in opposition to each other.

There is still another difference where, if people adopt a pronounced preference for one over the other position, they are likely to stress each other. This is between those who like to keep life under control, living in a planned, orderly way; and those who like to remain open to whatever comes along, just going with the flow. It is the contrast between those who like an organised, structured lifestyle and those who prefer a more spontaneous and flexible one.

The orderly ones are those who press for a settlement of any matter, sometimes even before there is sufficient information to make a good decision. They like things to be neatly concluded so that they know where they are, sometimes even preferring a poor decision to none at all. In the decision-making process they may be in danger of pressing for a premature closure. They reason that people can always make a decision to change a decision if necessary, but that if no decision is made there is the danger that nothing at all will be done. They have a point.

Those who prefer a flexible lifestyle generally like to delay making decisions, preferring to keep their options open as long as possible. In fact these two groups even have different concepts of what a decision actually is. The orderly group see decisions almost as tramlines from which one cannot depart unless the points are dearly changed, whereas the flexible group see 'decisions' as guidelines only. They reason that decisions must be provisional because, of course, they have to be capable of being changed when further information comes to light. They are so used to going with the flow and adapting as they go along, that they are often unaware when their stance has changed. Even when they are aware, they may forget to communicate this vital change to others.

The orderly types tend to make plans and stick to them. They like to be in control of their lives, and sometimes to keep the world around them in order too. Unless they learn to loosen up and give a bit they can become rigidly set in their ways. There is also the danger that they can seem to be dictatorial. The flexible types like to remain open to whatever possibilities come along; they tend to take on too much and may seem to be always in a rush. It is as though for them the deadline is the moment to begin an assignment, and unless they correct this tendency they can become unreliable.

Given these differences it is not surprising that how one group likes to conduct their lives is exactly what stresses people in the other group. Orderly people are stressed by indecision, loose ends, changing decisions (without clear, good reasons) and disorder. Flexible people are stressed by being tied down, by fussy detail, immutable decisions and tradition. They tend to be unhappy with deadlines and work that is unvarying and overscheduled; while orderly people dislike unpunctuality and ambiguity in any form.

One way to help lessen these stresses is to celebrate the differences, instead of concentrating on the difficulties people may have with each other. The decisiveness of the one complements the flexibility of the other; the information gathered by the latter types provides material upon which the former can make their decisions. The orderly types can help the others to be a little less random, while the flexible in turn can help the orderly ones not to become too rigid.

There is always a danger that some people will be tempted to dig their toes in and stubbornly stick to their own preferred way of doing things, and even perhaps exaggerate them in defiance or defence. Such a reaction does nothing to help remove the straws of irritation that tend to accumulate whenever people live or work with those who function differently from them. It is a more creative and constructive use of difference to learn from it, to welcome it as a bonus, and not let it become a bone of contention.

One last word of warning. While it is important to know, value and utilise our own particular way of doing things, we must never use any particular personality trait as an excuse. Turning up late and saying airily, 'I can't help it, I'm the type that just goes with the flow', is not likely to ease a tense situation. Far better to assume responsibility for the effect this trait has on others, and take steps to correct the bias whenever it inconveniences them. Something like, 'I'm so sorry, I was trying to fit in too much as usual, I really must learn it can't be done', is more likely to take the stress out of the situation.

What Puts Pressure on Different People Types

EXTRAVERTS
Lack of spoken response
Silence Slowness
Isolation Inactivity
Reserve
Delay

INTROVERTS
Lack of time to think
Chatter Being rushed
Crowds Immediacy
Exuberance
Instant demands
Interruptions

FACTUAL TYPES
Lack of clear instructions
Inconsistency Unpredictability
Speculation Imprecision
Innovation
Think tank meetings

INTUITIVE TYPES
Too many precise instructions
Rigidity Predictability
Detail Excess facts
Routine
Finance/fact meetings

ANALYTICAL 'HEAD' TYPES
Emotional expression
Subjectivity Discoursiveness
Inefficiency Woolly thinking
Conciliation

FEELING 'HEART' TYPES
Impersonal stance
Detachment Curtness
Lack of harmony Hostility
Confrontation

ORDERLY LIFESTYLE
Indecision Loose ends
Unstructured time
Unpunctuality Ambiguity
Randomness Novelty
Disorder

FLEXIBLE LIFESTYLE
Being tied down Fussiness
Timetables
Deadlines Precision
Routine Tradition
Rigidity

SEARCHING QUESTIONS

1. Do you recognise your own predominant traits?
If so, cherish the strengths of your 'type', and try to avoid the accompanying pitfalls.

2. Do you think that you recognise the 'type' of any of your friends, relatives or workmates?
If so, do not pigeonhole them. Honour the ways in which they differ from you. They are likely to complement your own traits.

3. When something about an individual irritates you, is it that you detect in them a characteristic of your own, that you dislike? If so, you probably disown it in yourself, and disapprove of it when you meet it in others. Or is that irritating characteristic in another something that you lack, and would do well to learn?

4. Can you see the positive side of whatever characteristics irritate you?

NOTES

1. Many centres around the country run courses on understanding personality, using the Myers-Briggs Type Indicator™. A list can be found in *Retreats*, published each year by The Retreat Association, Tel: (01494) 433004, Web: www.retreats.org.uk
CWR also run MBTI courses. See back of book or visit www.cwr.org.uk

2. I have chosen to spell extravert with an 'a', and introvert with an 'o', to emphasise their difference. Both are acceptable, although it is more usual to stick to either 'a' or 'o' for both.

7. THE COMMUNICATIONS CATCH

'When I use a word,' Humpty Dumpty said in rather a
scornful tone, 'it means just what I choose it to mean –
neither more nor less.'

Lewis Carroll, *Through the Looking Glass*

While people of different personality types do not wilfully manipulate
single words in such an idiosyncratic way, they are nonetheless
prone to misunderstand what others say. What is actually said by
the speaker is all too frequently not what is inferred, and therefore
received, by the listener. We will look at some of the misunderstandings that commonly occur and that can be the last straw to an
already hassled person. Fortunately, with good will, humour and a
modicum of understanding they can generally be laughed off, and
even enjoyed as part of the rich diversity of humankind.

At times the very energetic verbal presentation of extraverts,
and the silent thinking within, that is characteristic of introverts,
can be very frustrating each to the other. The extraverts' habit of
speaking all their thoughts aloud while they are working out their
answer to a question, often leaves the introverts confused. 'For
goodness sake, make up your mind and say what you mean. First
you said this, then you said that, and now you seem to be saying
something totally different again, and I just don't know what you
want', is a common response. However, as they are introverts they
are very likely to think but not enunciate their bewilderment under
such a barrage, so the extravert is apt to remain ignorant of the fact
that he has not actually been heard. That which was spoken has not
in fact been truly communicated.

Introverts on the other hand are generally quite content when
they know what they think about any matter, whether or not there
is anyone around to whom they can express the result of their

deliberations. It takes energy and is an effort for them to speak out, just as keeping silent is actually an exertion for extraverts, and diminishes their drive. Both need to understand and make allowances for the very different ways each has of processing their responses.

One day while waiting for a train deep in London's Underground system, a foreigner approached a friend of mine and asked the way to her destination. Immersed in her own thoughts, and not knowing the way, my friend silently walked over to the map on the wall to look it up but when she turned back to show the way, the enquirer had gone. On reflection my friend realised that, typical introvert, she had not even acknowledged the other person's question and must have seemed very rude, just walking away like that!

An extravert in such a situation would have kept up a running commentary, something like, 'Oh, I've never been there myself so I don't know but there's usually a map in these places, yes, look, it's over there, I'll just go and have a look, why don't you come too, where are you from? Been in London long? This your first visit? Oh dear I can't find it, let's look at the Piccadilly line, no, it's not there, ah, here it is. You change at …' and so on.

People approached in unguarded moments respond spontaneously, in the way most natural to them. It is when a person's guard is down, on holiday, say, or when they are taken by surprise, that their inherent reactions come to the fore. The very unexpectedness of a response, or its inappropriateness, or the fact that in the circumstances it is singularly unhelpful, is the sort of thing that causes resentment and misunderstanding. Sometimes things that in themselves are very minor can indeed be the last straw to someone in a hurry, already heavily burdened about other matters, or just generally stressed. The trigger is so often out of all proportion to the friction it causes.

During the process of socialisation and education most people learn to adapt their innate approach in order to accommodate the needs of others much of the time. Extraverts are able, at times, to moderate the vigour of their presentation, and the loquaciousness of their replies. It is possible for introverts to make the effort to extravert themselves a little, and share something of their thoughts and feelings. For both, these are learned responses, and as such may well desert people at critical moments; especially personal moments that are not discernible to others, and so the lapse in expected behaviour is liable to become an irritant.

Anyone who has ever attended a meeting, be it of a club, committee, church or any other group, will realise that there are two other distinct types of people there. Factual people can spot the smallest discrepancy in an obscure footnote to the accounts. Such an error is immensely important to them, and they save many a situation by being vigilant. Intuitive types are generally disinterested, if not frankly bored, in the proceedings at that stage but suddenly become animated when ideas, dreams and plans for the future are discussed.

As the theme changes, the factual group are quite likely to be perplexed, for they will suddenly have lost their landmarks. They are being asked to switch and look at unfamiliar, often highly imaginative, broad concepts. Both are distinct talents that are equally needed in any organisation, team or family. Factual types help to keep the speculation of the intuitives within bounds, by pointing out specific flaws and asking detailed practical questions. They want to know 'awkward' things like how much the whole thing is likely to cost, where the money is expected to come from, and what about any legal restrictions. All this can seem like nothing but obstruction to the more intuitive types, who are inclined to interpret such a practical approach as throwing cold water on their dreams.

These two groups may be having difficulty in communicating with each other because they look at any proposal from such different perspectives. Factual people tend to be realists. They need to be shown that the overall plan is feasible, and that when it is broken down into implemental stages each is a workable proposition. It helps them to be given specific examples of what is being discussed, and where something like it has been done successfully before. The voice of experience is very important to them.

All that can be a bit tedious to intuitive types, who are more likely to be fired up by a new and challenging concept that stretches their imagination. They respond to hunches and broad ideas, to what might be possible, and they do not want their dreams to be dragged down by detail. These two groups can be very creative together when they recognise and utilise the very different gifts they each have, and are able to work together harmoniously. If the factual people can allow the intuitives to dream for a while, these 'thinker-uppers' can provide the more practical 'getter-doners' with interesting things to get on and do.

Even the conversational style of these two groups is very different. The factual people call a spade a spade, neither more nor less. They are brief, direct and often very literal, especially when under stress. There was an example of this on Denis Norden's programme of TV out-takes, *It'll Be Alright on the Night*. The interviewee had evidently had an horrific experience. He was asked, 'So what state were you in?' to which he replied something like, 'Oh, I don't know, Idaho I think.' Then there was the woman, unused to travelling, who was purchasing her rail ticket at the usual little window and on being told, 'Change at Edinburgh,' firmly replied, 'No, I'd rather have it now, please.'

Intuitive people often infuriate others because they frequently leave their sentences in mid-air, expecting the listener to be able to guess the rest. They are at best relatively indirect and imprecise, tending to give complex answers to simple questions. There is a saying 'Ask them the time, and they'll tell you how a clock works.' You then know a lot more about clocks, but not whether it is time to put the supper in the oven.

When driving a factual friend along a series of roundabouts I asked, 'Is this the one?' meaning, but not actually articulating, 'the one where we take the third exit instead of the second.' I expected her to intuit what I wanted to know! We were approaching the second exit as I spoke, and it was the roundabout where we needed the third exit. She said, 'No', meaning 'We do not take this exit', but I took this to mean 'Not the roundabout where we leave the series'. Accordingly, I took the second exit, and immediately heard her gasp of astonishment. We both laughed, as we realised this was yet another instance of miscommunication. I turned the car round, and all was well between us. It could have been a very different story if we had been at odds with each other before we set out. Such a little instance can indeed be another straw heaping up on a pile of minor misunderstandings, until it topples right over and one or other person makes a snappy remark that ruins the day.

Factual people tend to communicate in a straightforward way. They give, and like to hear from others, the origin of the topic under discussion, tending to go into considerable detail. They begin at the beginning of a story or plan, and give it in consecutive order, with few omissions, and hence little is left to the imagination of the hearer. One of the things they have to learn is that all this detail is apt to cause the more intuitive types to switch off, for they really need to let their imagination roam a little to maintain their interest in the topic.

Intuitive people for their part have to learn to give some of the background to their thinking, rather than launching straight into the middle of what is, at that moment, a somewhat rudimentary idea. They also have to watch their tendency to leave many of their sentences unfinished. They like to deal in generalities more than specifics, and are prone to express themselves figuratively. Communication with factual types is enhanced when they learn to limit their use of metaphor, and to remember that factual people tend to be literal and precise.

Communication between two individuals with such dissimilar outlooks will be more productive when each modifies their natural tendencies, to take account of the needs of the other person. Often when a friend and I are talking she will break off and say, 'Oh, but you don't want all these details, do you?' She is right, they only serve to confuse me. For my part there are occasions when it is clear to me that I have not conveyed to her the least idea of what I am trying to say. A moment's reflection reminds me that I have launched into a tale without giving her any facts at all. She has neither the beginning of the story, nor its setting, and is rightly bewildered.

We have learned a lot from each other. Instead of flatly turning down some half-baked new idea of mine, she has learned to say something like 'Well it might work if …', or 'Have you thought about such and such?' This tactful way of pointing out some specific gaping holes in my proposal, rather than dismissing it entirely, stimulates me to try and fill those gaps, then we repeat the process until between us we have something that satisfies us both. But when either of us is tired, or taken by surprise, she is likely to dismiss my ideas as unworkable 'pie in the sky', and I am inclined to accuse her of being a wet blanket or a stick in the mud!

An additional source of unintentional annoyance is the cool delivery and impersonal stance usually adopted by people of an analytical turn of mind, even at home or with their closest friends. They tend to put their point of view briefly and bluntly, seeing issues as black or white, right or wrong, with little apparent realisation that there might be an intermediate position.

All this is in such marked contrast to the personal and often impassioned approach of the 'heart before head' people. As they see most issues in shades of grey, rather than in absolutes of black or white, they are more inclined to ask whether people will like or dislike any course of action. That is generally of more importance to them than whether it is in itself a right or wrong action or decision. Since they always look at things from the human situation they will want to take into account any mitigating circumstances. Analytical people, who tend to put abstract principle before people issues, are likely to consider them irrelevant.

When called upon to appraise a situation or a piece of work, analytical people are likely to launch straight into a critique, without any preliminaries. They do this from the best of motives, reasoning that when anyone has done a good job it is a service to that person if they point out something that is not quite up to the standard of all the rest. They reason that when what they have pinpointed is rectified, then that which was merely a good job will become an excellent piece of work. Excellence and efficiency are two things that they themselves constantly strive to achieve, and so they make the assumption that these things are also of prime importance to everyone else. It is often hard for them to realise that many people want to be valued for who they are, as persons, and not merely for the things that they can accomplish.

'Heart' people are all too liable to take the objectively offered critique as not only a criticism, but a personal one at that. Their own approach is usually to offer some appreciation of at least one aspect of the matter under discussion, before they get around to voicing any critical comments. They also prefer to focus on areas where agreement does exist, before they get down to addressing controversial issues.

Even the simple matter, in our culture, of 'oiling' the contact between people, whether in person or in writing, seems to be largely ignored by analytical people. They use those magic words 'please' and 'thank you' very sparingly. Indeed, I have heard one such person consider the matter and then say, 'No, of course I don't say "please" to my secretary when I am asking her to do what is clearly her job, I would only say that when I am asking her to do more. And I would only thank her when she has done something more than is required of her, not for just doing her job.'

To the 'head' people this is how it should be, but to 'heart before head' ones it comes across as brusque to the point of being impolite. And that does nothing to reduce or ease whatever other tensions may be around between them. Indeed it can suddenly be the last straw. On the other hand, the frequent use of those accepted politenesses by 'heart' people, while natural to them, is at best unnecessary and can at times seem ingratiatingly irritating to the 'head' brigade. And that is between people of the same culture and much the same background. There may also be pinpricks arising from personal mannerisms or subcultural foibles; the opportunity for causing unwitting offence between people from different countries and cultures is almost boundless.

What is courteous and designed to show respect in one society, is gauche and ungracious, if not frankly offensive, in another. In any setting where no one takes the trouble to point out these discrepancies the offending behaviour continues to add a quite unnecessary stress. All it takes is good-willed communication between the people concerned. Lack of discussion often allows small straws to build up into sizeable bundles, when they could so easily be removed one by one.

Even exactly the same word can be charged with a completely different meaning, depending on the preoccupations and interests of both sender and receiver. Context and frame of reference are everything, as depicted in a cartoon I saw some years ago in the financial section of a Saturday newspaper. It showed a power-dressed woman visiting her husband in hospital and saying as she approached his bedside, 'I can't tell you how relieved I am, darling. When my secretary said there had been a crash … at first I thought she meant the market!'

A final twist to the way communications can miss the mark, though by no means the last word on the subject, is the way those of an orderly lifestyle can exasperate their more flexible colleagues. This works in reverse too. They each have different expectations of how conversation, or correspondence, should be conducted. Orderly people want things stated in a straightforward way, with clear statements, and matters brought to a definite conclusion. This is in marked contrast to the flexible people who dislike being pinned down too firmly. In trying to keep their options open they are often ambiguous, and so leave ample room for misunderstanding.

In any communication we have to realise that even the most neutral words and expressions are subject to instant, unconscious interpretation by the hearer or reader. We hear and see things through the veil of our own past experiences, and colour them with any number of assumptions. To avoid these pitfalls it is often necessary to ask clarifying questions, in order to find out what the speaker wishes to convey. What we hear is so often not quite, or even not at all, what was meant.

When we are the ones making the communication, we can assist the process by putting things in two ways. First, and most naturally, we will express ourselves according to our own personality. Then it is helpful to rephrase things in a way which will be enlightening for those whose outlook is the opposite to our own. It may not be easy or comfortable to do so, but it will pay dividends in terms of improved communication.

When I ask my factual friend, 'Shall we go the longer way next weekend?' I am being incomprehensible to her. She lives in the present moment and has difficulty in suddenly switching to the future. Also 'longer way' is too vague for her to express an opinion. As I remember these things I quickly add, 'When we go to Eccsford to do the Basics Course next Friday I would like to leave earlier than last year and go on the quieter country roads, instead of all motorways. We would need to leave at 2pm to enjoy the journey.' When she is reminded of the setting, with this information she can decide whether she can be ready for 2pm, and whether speed or enjoyment are more important for her.

As a 'heart' person I am inclined to ask others what they feel about a proposition. Such a question is unlikely to engage the interest of 'head' people, but if I ask what they think (not feel) about the matter then I am more likely to gain their attention.

Successful communication depends on a number of factors

other than words and their interpretation. The eloquent language of the body is now recognised as a potent communicator, especially the aspect of eye contact. Its absence gives a clear message of avoidance or evasion, although it leaves the reason for such action in doubt. It may be due to preoccupation with other matters; to disinclination to engage with you or with anyone else, at this stage; or a number of other interpretations. To avoid misinterpretation it is always important to check out what is going on in the mind of the other.

Communication Characteristics

EXTRAVERTS
Running commentary ALOUD
Respond QUICKLY
SHARING imperative
Prefer verbal communication

INTROVERTS
SILENT thinking within
REFLECT first
THINK TIME essential
Apparently DETACHED
Like things in writing

FACTUAL PEOPLE
Straightforward Precise
Facts Details Examples
Little omitted
Refer to:
Experience The known
Want a proposal to be:
Realistic Workable

INTUITIVE PEOPLE
Imaginative Metaphorical
Concepts Ideas Broad picture
Sentences unfinished
Refer to:
Hunches The possible
Want a proposal to be:
Novel Challenging

ANALYTICAL 'HEAD' PEOPLE
Objective Brief Concise
Present goals
Task oriented
Cool, impersonal delivery
Ignore social 'oil'

FEELING 'HEART' PEOPLE
Subjective Anecdotal
Establish relationship
People oriented
Impassioned, personalised delivery
Offer pleasantries

TRUTH paramount	TACT essential
Critique Point out flaws	Avoid confrontation Appreciate Areas of agreement

ORDERLY LIFESTYLE	**FLEXIBLE LIFESTYLE**
People expect:	*People expect:*
Conclusions Clarity	Options kept open
Results	Ambiguity Enjoyment

SEARCHING QUESTIONS

Using the list of pairs above consider the following questions:

1. Which one of each pair most describes your way of communicating?
2. Is there any pair where you naturally tend towards all of one side, and none of the other?
   If so it may be helpful for you to pay more attention to the neglected side.
3. Are you stressed by someone who communicates mainly in the style of one half of one or more of these pairs?
   Work out how to ask that person to help you by using a bit more of the complementary approach.
   For example: If someone communicates mainly from the left side of the list, and you incline more towards the right side, tell them you find it difficult to give instant answers. Let them know that you need time to consider your reply. Tell them that you find too many facts all at once confusing, until you have grasped the overall picture. You might even be able to get across to them that their impersonal, detached approach does not help.
   NB. People may operate from either side of any pair; only a few do so from all left, or all right sides. The example was chosen for simplicity, not because it occurs frequently!

8. MAKING FRIENDS WITH TIME

I have read a variety of books and articles on the subject of effective time management. There are gems to be gleaned from each of them, but overall I am left feeling unsatisfied and dissatisfied. I have come to the conclusion that the most helpful comment on the subject comes not from that type of book but from another of Lewis Carroll's characters, this time in *Alice in Wonderland*:

> 'If you knew Time as well as I do,' said the Hatter, 'you wouldn't talk about wasting *it*. It's *him*.'

Later on the story continues,

> 'Ah! That accounts for it,' said the Hatter. 'He won't stand beating. Now, if you only kept on good terms with him, he'd do almost anything you liked with the clock.'

What we each need to do 'to keep on good terms with him' will depend on a great many considerations.

As we go through successive life stages, the differing needs and responsibilities mean that our attitude to time, and our use of it, needs to change in line with our changing circumstances. Throughout our early growing years there is, hopefully, a gradual assumption of personal responsibility for how we spend 'our' time. Along with this, it is expected that there will also develop an increasing awareness of the need to respect and, where appropriate, fit into the timings of other people. For some, the transition from school to the freer atmosphere of college may be a problem. It is all part of the learning process. At this stage, society and families generally make allowances for difficulties that individuals may encounter as they negotiate unfamiliar freedom and responsibilities. The juggling with those two concepts, freedom versus responsibility, continues in various ways as we progress through life.

People with different types of personality view the whole concept of time in quite distinct ways. Sometimes they seem to be looking at it through contrasting, even divergent, lenses. In learning to make friends with time we need to understand our own particular concept of it. Then each of us has to learn to recognise and respect the dissimilar ways of viewing time that may be taken by other people. We need to appreciate and honour these often contra-distinct viewpoints, even if we cannot fully understand them.

Whatever attitude we ourselves take regarding the whole complex matter of time, we must recognise that it will not be universally understood or appreciated. When the various different views are unrecognised and unacknowledged they give rise to a great deal of unnecessary friction. Sometimes the irritation that they cause is out of all proportion to the actual differences in outlook. Yet until there is some recognition of the divergence in outlook, the constant irritation can indeed be the last straw at times of stress. Removing that straw of provocation is one small but vital step towards better working and living relationships.

As Professor Higgins sighed despairingly in *My Fair Lady*, 'Oh, why can't a woman be more like a man!' We all wish, secretly or with varying degrees of openness, that other people would take the same stance that we do. In some respects, and especially at times of stress, life would be so much simpler if only all of 'them' could manage to be like us, or to do things our way. On the other hand, the world would also be exceedingly dull for many people. It would certainly lack colour, vitality, interest – and challenge.

However widely our ideas on the whole subject of time may diverge, we all have to exercise some discipline in the matter. Which particular aspects of the subject require our restraint, or our effort, will depend, amongst other things, on our personality make-up. In his commentary on the broad and narrow way (*Gospel of Matthew, Volume I*) William Barclay writes,

> Nothing was ever achieved without discipline; and many an athlete and many a man has been ruined because he abandoned discipline and let himself grow slack. Coleridge is the supreme tragedy of indiscipline. Never did so great a mind produce so little. He left Cambridge University to join the army; he left the army because, in spite of his erudition, he could not rub down a horse; he returned to Oxford and left without a degree. He began a paper called *The Watchman* which lived for ten numbers and then died. It has been said of him: 'He lost himself in visions of work to be done, that always remained to be done.' In his head and in his mind he had all kinds of books, as he said himself, 'completed save for the transcription'. 'I am on the eve,' he says, 'of sending to the press two octavo volumes.' But the books were never composed outside Coleridge's mind, because he would not face the discipline of sitting down to write them out.[1]

We are all prone to procrastinate, but the type of activity we tend to put off will be different depending on where our interests and values mainly lie. These are largely what determine our priorities. All of us are more likely to get on with the things that interest us, and there are few people without the tendency to shelve the things that they find difficult or distasteful. However, as the old saying goes, 'One person's meat is another person's poison'.

Different ways of viewing time are often a very real issue between people. It is a source of argument at home, at work and wherever people need to interact with each other. Most of us will get on and deal first with those things that are of importance in our scheme of things or that seem to come naturally to us. And it is an equally natural tendency to defer tackling things that go against the grain in some way, unless we have been rigorously trained to do otherwise. No one has the monopoly on stalling over issues that they find disagreeable.

Extraverts are most likely to procrastinate about anything that requires them to leave the convivial crowd and go off to work alone. This may be especially difficult for them when being alone requires them to reflect on their own internal processes. Introverts are much more prone to procrastinate about meeting others, especially when this means doing so in what, to them, is a large crowd. Viewing exactly the same number of people, an extravert is quite likely to say, 'What a pity there aren't more people here'!

Because factual people tend to live so very much in the present moment it can be very difficult for some of them to project themselves forward. They are reluctant to consider the future. Because it has not yet arrived it can be hard for them to even contemplate it. They are liable to procrastinate about planning much beyond their 'now'. By contrast, intuitive people, with their eye on the future, may find it hard to live in the present moment, as the factual people do so successfully. And sometimes the past is even harder for them to spend any effort on. They can easily procrastinate about taking time to review the past, their own past, and learn the lessons it has for them.

Analytical people, with their emphasis on logical reasoning and debate, on excellence and reliability, have a tendency to procrastinate in matters regarding personal relationships. For them, people issues are just one among many other factors to be weighed and observed objectively, and they tend to put off dealing with personal issues.

In marked contrast to them are the 'heart' people. They value harmonious interpersonal relationships so highly that they generally put off tackling anything that might rock this particular boat. They do not like to engage in confrontation, and are likely to put that on their back burner for as long as possible.

People who favour an orderly and predictable lifestyle generally take a serious view about finishing work and chores. They tend to give a low priority to leisure pursuits, unless these are undertaken for health reasons when they may well work hard at them. These people are likely to procrastinate about allowing themselves any real relaxation or personal pleasure.

People who adopt a flexible lifestyle differ, in that they generally set a high value on enjoyment, and are likely to mix work and pleasure as they go along. Perhaps J.M. Barrie had them in mind when he wrote 'Nothing is really work unless you would rather be doing something else.' The thing these people find hard, and so are likely to procrastinate about, is making decisions. They are likely to waste time by dithering, and often find that their decisions are made by default, because the time for taking positive action has run out. They are likely to have so many enticing options before them that the decision-making process can be helped by asking them what they do *not* want. When some of the endless possibilities are ruled out it may be easier for them to select what it is that they *do* want.

We can all delay tackling the things that cause us a problem, but what seems like a huge mountain to climb for one group of people may well be meat and drink to another. In order not to get exasperated by the vagaries of people who tend to irritate us we need to try and comprehend their values and motivation. This is especially important in the contentious issue regarding the use, and relative value, of time. When we can see our differences as valid, rather than irresponsible or inefficient whims, some angst will go out of the clash.

People with an extravert tendency, pulled by their need to interact with others, can seem, to the more introvert inclined, to be actually invading their private space and their time. Introvert people often find it hard to forgive them for what seems, from their point of view, to be a definite intrusion. Once extraverts are reminded of the introvert need for adequate reflection time, they really will try – when they remember – not to rush in where angels fear to tread. Time and opportunity for reflection are such absolute necessities for introverts that they are liable to become both tired and harassed by those who seem to them to be importunate, invasionary, people. They themselves can get so lost in what they are doing that they are at times apt to forget the outside world and its deadlines. This absorption in what they are doing at the moment can sometimes be so great that others may feel jealous, and of little or no importance to them.

For some people it is not so much a matter of viewing time differently, as of actually seeming to live in quite distinct time warps. There are those factual people who perceive time almost as this present moment only. The past is over and done with, so events that occurred in it may be hard for them to recall. The future has not yet arrived, so it has no significance for them. They are the 'No time like the present' people for whom 'now' generally is the only time of which they are really aware.

By contrast there are also the more intuitive 'there and then' people. These are the ones who seem to be always planning for the future, even seeming to live in it rather than in the present moment. They are generally into so many possibilities that 'real time' for them is either irrelevant or seems to be endless. They are the ones who often genuinely believe that they, and therefore others, can always somehow fit in something more. 'Always time for one more thing' seems to be the unquestioned motto they live by, and it especially applies to those last five minutes before any deadline.

The future, and their dreams for it, is so authentic to them that sometimes they do not know whether they have actually done something or merely considered doing so. That is the time zone they naturally inhabit. It is hard work for them to concentrate on the present. Often the sanctity of the present moment is something that eludes them, unless they actively seek and receive it.

Analytical people, who invest heavily in understanding and debating weighty issues, will often disregard the need to also work at achieving good working relationships. In their desire to get a job done, and on time, they have a tendency to overlook the human needs of human beings. From their perspective, efficient completion of a job is more important than the welfare of the people carrying out the various tasks necessary to get the job done. Not surprisingly some of those workers are likely to feel used, even abused. They feel disregarded in the pressure of time.

A 'people' person, facing a comparable dilemma, would probably prefer to countenance some slippage in the time scale if that would make for a more harmonious family or workforce. The analytical and the 'people' person appraise the situation they are called upon to deal with from the standpoint of totally different priorities. The diametrically opposite view each takes depends on whether it is task completion that is of paramount importance, or the people carrying out the task.

Analytical people will benefit from learning about, and training themselves to take more account of, people-centred issues so that they are a little less driven by time constraints alone. Appreciating the valid needs and concerns of individuals just does not come naturally to them. Those who are more people-oriented on the other hand will benefit from learning to balance their concern for people with an appreciation of the objective principles behind some contentious issues, of which time is surely one. Then both will be more able to begin to understand the point of view of the other.

When they can both accept that they each have different, but equally valid and equally useful, points of view, one more 'straw' of irritation will hopefully have been lifted from the pile.

Orderly types seem to regard time as a fixed entity. It is just another aspect of life to be managed; it is yet one more thing to channel and keep under their control. They generally do not like to be taken by surprise or caught unawares, and so they tend to keep a close watch on time. They are often keenly aware of their own use of time, and they may be unable to resist trying to influence others towards their way of regarding the issue.

Time for them is a serious matter, a commodity to be utilised, something to be used well and fruitfully. There must generally be something to show for their use of it, some tangible result at the end of any particular period. They are the people who not only tend to make lists in order to help them fit everything into their schedule, but they make use of them, sometimes so much so that anything inadvertently left off the list may not get done.

Such people like to fulfil their obligations before they can think of enjoying themselves. They prefer to finish all work before even considering the expenditure of time and energy on what to them are discretionary, and privileged, recreational activities. When people with this attitude to time live or work together they are likely to reinforce these workaholic tendencies in each other. They are likely to have, or make, little time for leisure because the notion of 'play' has such a low priority for them.

'All work and no play makes Jack a dull boy, and Jill a dull girl' is indeed a danger for workaholic-inclined people. Another hazard is the possibility of getting stuck in a rut, always on the treadmill of serious and productive pursuits with no let up, no lightening of their earnest outlook. They need to give themselves, and each other, permission and positive encouragement to take a more light-hearted approach on occasions.

Not surprisingly, it is generally people like this who write most of the books on time management and those who do not write them will eagerly buy them, and adhere to the principles laid out.

That whole attitude is quite foreign to the flexible types who prefer to go through life welcoming whatever the great sea of life washes their way. They are more interested in enjoyment than in control and tend to adapt to things more or less as they find them. Their life is characterised by the underlying belief that things will generally work out all right. These people tend to dislike rigid schedules, preferring to be free to respond to whatever seems best, or most expedient, when the time comes. Their discomfort at the prospect of being too firmly tied down to the exact minute is also shown in their use of 'ish' time. They are likely to make arrangements to meet friends at 'sixish' rather than at six o'clock precisely.

These are the people who always seem to think that they can get more done in any span of time than is remotely possible, and so they are perpetually in a rush. It has been said of them, 'The deadline is the moment to begin'. Sometimes they do buy books on time management or achieving an orderly life. They are genuinely interested in the notion and the possibilities described, although for them it is somewhat like learning a foreign language. Once the interesting, and therefore the easy, bits have been read the rest is likely to be put to one side to be considered later. They have yet to learn that 'later' never arrives. There is an essential question for them to ask themselves whenever they lay something aside, meaning to return to it at some other time. It is simple and direct: 'If not now; when?'

Two people with this flexible attitude towards time will have, when they live or work together, a hard job getting things done on schedule. They will also often, but not reliably always, have difficulty in arriving at places on time, whether for work or play. Not surprisingly, such people are likely to be irritated by what seems to them the absurd and unnecessary precision of the punctual, orderly group. Viewing as they do the whole matter of time from such a different angle they are likely to consider as nit-picking the exactitude of those whom they secretly regard as control freaks. Likewise, their own casual approach is likely to infuriate the more punctilious people, who tend to be ruffled by their seeming carelessness.

Redeem the Time

1. Different personalities perceive and handle time differently:

Extraverts – Can seem to invade the time of others.
Introverts – Can get so absorbed in what they are doing that they forget other things and people exist.

Factual people – 'No time like the present.'
Intuitive people – 'Always time for one more thing.'

Analytical people – In their need to get a job done well, and on time, they may disregard the people doing the work.
'Heart' people – In their overriding concern for people, they may overlook the reality of time constraints.

Orderly people – See time as a commodity to be managed seriously. They must beware of becoming control freaks.
Flexible people – See time as approximate. They must beware of becoming careless.

2. We can all procrastinate, but tend to do so about different things:

Extraverts – Working, or being alone, for too long.
Introverts – Meeting people, especially in a crowd.

Factual people – Forward planning; it takes them into the future.
Intuitive people – Reviewing the past, to learn its lessons.

Analytical people – Developing personal relationships.
'Heart' people – Confrontation, for fear of upsetting others.

Orderly people – Recreation, and personal pleasure.
Flexible people – Making, and keeping, decisions. They dither, and run out of time.

SEARCHING QUESTIONS

1. Which one of each pair in No 1 (above) most nearly describes you?
If you have absolutely no inclination towards the other one of any pair, consider what small concessions you might sometimes make in that direction. Then try and actually make these on occasions.

2. Do you procrastinate?
About what?
Work out ways to overcome this tendency.
For example: If you procrastinate about taking any recreation, decide what you would like to do, and when. Then put it in your diary, and honour the commitment.
If you procrastinate about making decisions, watch out for this and decide to decide. Recognising your tendency is part way to dealing with it.

NOTE

1.   William Barclay, *Gospel of Matthew, Volume 1* (Edinburgh: St Andrew's Press, 1997).

9. NOT ANOTHER CHANGE!

Change is a natural process. Day is softened by twilight before progressing into the darkness of night, which comes before another day dawns. There is the longer lunar cycle, which nowadays seldom affects urban dwellers directly. The regular cycle of the seasons, however erratic it may seem to get, is something that does impinge upon most of us. We need regular punctuation marks in our lives.

However much we may try to keep things the same we cannot do so, for change is a part of the world in which we live. But you can have too much of a good thing. The philosopher Edmund Burke said of change that it is 'the most powerful law of nature'. Like all forces of nature we have to learn to live with it. We also have to learn to regulate our individual exposure to change according to our own capacity and disposition.

Too much change in a given period of time is stressful for anyone, whoever they are. However, what is too much change in too short a time span for one person may well be too little change in too long a time for another. Individuals have very different capacities for responding to change in a creative and life-enhancing way.

Sooner or later we will all reach a stage when enough change is enough. As we approach our own individual 'enough change for now' zone, we begin to become resistant to any further changes, even if they will be in some other area of our lives. Our adaptability has been stretched far enough for the time being. If reorganisation, or some other restructuring, is causing considerable and perhaps prolonged disruption at work then most people are very relieved to get away to a scenario that is reliable and familiar. They head for home, the gym, church or the pub; anywhere where there are people who are dependable and stable, when currently the work environment is neither.

A prolonged period of uncertainty and change at work is

easier to handle when home and social situations are able to provide stability and an anchor. On the other hand when the disruption is at home, for whatever reason, then many people are glad to escape from it to the customary routine and reliable people at work. It is helpful to have stability in at least one area of our lives. We need a steadying influence that will provide a secure platform from which we can make the required adaptations in those areas that are in a state of flux. It is necessary to have some sure reference points while we cope with the changes.

Less radical changes at work may be just as stressful as the more sweeping ones for an individual who is currently adjusting to major changes in his personal and emotional life. It is all a question of how much change in how many areas of life there are in one time span. When there is uncertainty and worry at home, a bereavement, the birth of a child (especially the first), relationship or financial problems; all these and more will tend to make a person more vulnerable than they would otherwise be.

Change can naturally be stimulating as well as taxing. It provides us with a challenge that may provoke us to discover greater resources than we had previously been aware of. These resources are likely to be both within ourselves and around us. The very uncertainty of change can prompt us to question our values, our philosophy of life and our belief system. We can emerge with a stronger, more robust faith when we are forced to examine our foundation stone, the Rock who is Christ.

If the shifting sands of change reveal that our foundation is also insubstantial this presents us with the opportunity for some remedial work. It is only when we realise that perhaps we have not yet entered into a life-transforming and life-enhancing relationship with the living God that we are likely to seek Him. Seeking is the beginning of finding, and of being found.

There are, of course, certain stages in life when a degree of turbulence is to be expected. The hormonal, maturational and cultural changes of adolescence; child bearing and rearing; mid-life; retirement; and the varying responsibilities we shoulder all demand considerable personal adaptation. How we react to unsettling events will depend in part on whether they are sought by us or imposed by circumstances. It will also be influenced by whether they come upon us suddenly or gradually, and whether they have been foreseen or are totally unexpected.

Adjusting to change cannot be a sudden occurrence. It is a process that inevitably takes time. Time: that elusive reality of which we never seem to have the right amount. In an age of instant coffee, instant meals, instant quotes over the phone or the internet, we are impatient with anything that cannot be achieved instantly, and preferably even sooner.

Part of that adjustment is the requirement to let go of at least some elements of the past, before we can reach out and take hold of the present. 'Present', as in time. We can only live in today; not yesterday which has already gone; not tomorrow, which has not yet arrived. Also 'present' as in gift. Few things in life are perfect, and few changes are achieved without a hiccup or two being encountered, so when facing change it is important to look for the potential gifts it may bring. However hard some aspects of the change may be, we must surely aim to maximise the possibilities for positive good that are part of the package deal. It won't bring Utopia, but it will bring scope for improvement in at least some areas.

That is one side of the coin called 'change'. On the other side are the disadvantages, the negative aspects, which are part of the cost of change. There is usually some loss involved. We lose our routine and our bearings. All those little daily actions which have become automatic no longer bring the expected result. We reach out for something as simple as an envelope and find it is no longer where we expect it to be. The office or kitchen layout is now completely different and it has to be re-learnt.

Sometimes almost every element of the daily routine has to

be mastered afresh. It takes time and can be a most exasperating procedure. Adjusting to change is a process, not an event. We cannot pick up the new procedures until we have fully let go of the old ones. This is a mini-death to those who find their security in routine. It is a case of new growth not being possible until the old has been allowed to die, or has been cut out, in order to make room for the new.

As well as losing our routine and the familiarity of knowing where things are and what to expect as we go round the next corner, most changes are likely to involve an alteration in relationships. People move away or move up the ladder. The person who was once a colleague may have become the boss, and so the relationship will inevitably be somewhat different from now on. Such changes are likely to be accompanied by a whole range of feelings, some of which will probably be at least partly denied. Ambivalence, the simultaneous existence of two conflicting desires, is likely to occur and will be hard to handle constructively. There is always the risk of some degree of conflict creeping in to distort the new connection between the parties. This possibility needs to be discussed openly between them in order to minimise any friction and covert antagonism.

Judicious planning can sometimes reduce the stress of cumulative changes. Some people like to pace the many little changes involved in accomplishing any major one so that, while they are coping with upheaval at work, things at home remain much as usual. They plan to make domestic changes either before or after those associated with their employment. Other people prefer to get as many changes as possible over all together, in as short a time as possible. For them, one big earthquake is better than many minor rumblings.

There is no ideal solution, no one recipe to suit all tastes. What is necessary is that the situation is thought through in the light of the many factors that will involve each individual who will be affected by the proposed changes. All the many straws that together make up the total burden need to be examined and dealt with in the best way possible, so that the entire load does not exceed the strength of this particular camel's back.

There is often a considerable gulf between those who decide to make changes, whether in a family or an organisation, and those who will be implementing the changes. The decision-makers have time to consider the matter from as many angles as they choose. They have the opportunity to gather and sift information, to assess the options and to define the goals. They tend to see only the eventual advantages and need to remember that changes, for the people required to implement them, actually create problems that were not there before. If the implementers have no chance to influence decisions along the way they may well become resentful.

Thorough discussion of the reasons behind any anticipated changes is always important. These should take place as early as possible and involve everyone if maximum co-operation is to be achieved. Co-operation does not necessarily mean the full agreement of every single person involved; that is probably an impossibility. The collaboration of most people can generally be secured if they consider that their views and needs have been properly considered, and the reasons for not being able to meet all of them are discussed.

When there is insufficient or perfunctory consultation there will always be some people who resort to passive non-cooperation. They may feel too insecure, insignificant and aggrieved at being overlooked to discuss their grievances openly, with the right people. The consequence is that they will be all too likely to quietly sabotage arrangements as a form of more or less unconscious revenge. The cumulative effect of minor things like failing to pass on messages, or to finish things quite on time, can be satisfyingly disruptive for such people.

During the planning stage, prior to implementing any changes, it is important to reduce uncertainty wherever possible. Get, and give, as much information as is feasible. If this is not done, there is a danger that the inevitable rumours will become reality in the minds of some people. At every stage, check and see that people understand what is going to happen, and why. Wherever it is possible to do so, let there be some options open to them, some room for personal choice, so that they do not feel trapped into an impersonal system.

During the actual implementation of any major changes, the process will go much more smoothly if the three 'Rs' are remembered. These principles apply equally to families, friendship groups, church life and big business. People appreciate some reward – the first R – for the dislocation they suffer, and for the extra effort they put in. This may be anything from a verbal 'thank you', to a well-presented written one, acknowledging their effort and its contribution to achieving the goal behind the changes. For mega upheavals, arrange a suitable treat; at work a bonus half-day would be much appreciated. Few people respond well to being taken for granted, or to being treated as mere cogs in a machine.

The second R is about rest and refreshment. When effort is being expended there must be adequate breaks, and these need to be flexible ones to fit in with the varying needs of different people. Some like to get as much done as possible in one go, working away at a steady pace before taking a longish break. Others prefer to work more in fits and starts, having several mini-breaks along the way to refresh them and to allow themselves to gather their next burst of energy. When people are able to work as much as possible according to their own style they will accomplish more in the long run, and will do so more effectively than when they have to tailor their contribution to a style that is alien to them.

The third R is about reducing or postponing whatever can be reduced or postponed, during a period of implementing major changes. Pruning out anything that is not essential to the main task of the moment allows people to concentrate on that alone. Having a limited objective is helpful. Being able to focus primarily on getting the changes completed is a very powerful incentive to get them finalised, or at least underway. The goal is not the changes themselves, but to achieve a resumption of the smooth running of the home, office or wherever.

As well as trying to regulate the overall change we are individually subject to during any one period, it is also important to know ourselves. We need to know, and work with, the strengths and weaknesses of our own characteristic attitude towards change.

Everyone needs to be given, or to gather for themselves, information about possible changes ahead. Extraverts will want plenty of opportunity to process their reactions aloud and to discuss the issues raised with other people. Introverts will benefit from having the information in writing, before they are expected to give an opinion on the matter. They will need time to digest it and reflect on the implications before they are able to give an adequately considered response.

Both extraverts and introverts will need understanding support if imminent changes involve relocating some distance away. The extraverts will miss their involvement in communal activities; the introverts are likely to take time to adjust to the prospect, for they will miss the familiar environment and trusted people.

Factual people will require detailed data, and specific examples of how the proposed changes will affect them, their particular work and the procedures with which they are familiar. Intuitive people are going to be more interested in the broad implications of the proposed changes, and the opportunities they are likely to bring.

Analytical people are unlikely to acquiesce to changes unless they are given logical reasons as to why those changes should be adopted at all, and why now. In fact they will need plenty of opportunities to put 'why' questions to the relevant people. They will bring to the debate a sense of fairness, and the need for justice and equality in implementing the changes.

'Heart' people are likely to focus their attention on personnel issues in general, and personal implications in particular. If their co-operation is to be gained it is essential that they have the experience of their concerns being heard and properly considered. If this does not happen there is a very real danger that the introverted ones in particular may become passive resisters, which will help no one.

The orderly people will probably want some sort of timetable of events, with a structure for each stage of implementing the changes. They may be helped by having phased goals along the way, so that at the completion of each stage they can have a sense of achievement and 'rightness'. However, the timetable must always be sufficiently elastic that the flexible people do not feel in an impossible straitjacket. It is helpful for them if there is some scope for initiative, and if they are encouraged to work through the changes in their own way.

One of the secrets in knowing how to manage the process of change is to know yourself and the other people who are involved in the changes. Some people are prone to make more starts than finishes. The extravert intuitive people with a flexible lifestyle are changers by nature. They are great at giving the initial vision. They bring enthusiasm to the project, which the extravert factual people with a flexible lifestyle soon catch, but neither are likely to be particularly good at seeing it through.

The ideas that have been tossed around need to be properly analysed and evaluated, something at which introverted analysts excel. If those ideas are then adopted in principle, the process of actually implementing them has to be organised. This is something that the extravert analyst with an orderly lifestyle can hardly resist doing. But they are inclined to be blunt, and even abrasive, in the process. They have a tendency to ride roughshod over anyone who does not see things as they do.

Clearly this is where the 'heart' people, the harmonisers, come into their own. Whether extravert or introvert, their strongest desire is for people to be at ease, so they will ensure that personnel issues are adequately addressed.

There are almost bound to be some who are initially most resistant to change. When their reluctance is overcome they will probably be the key people in actually implementing and managing the changes. They are likely to be the introverted, factual people who like an orderly lifestyle, and are happy to bring order out of chaos. They are the only ones who will take care of all the necessary details that the rest are likely to overlook.

So everyone has a role to play, once their gifts are identified, and used correctly.

Managing Change

1. Adjusting to change is a process, not an event. It takes time.
2. Plan adequately. Pace the number of changes in any given time span. If there is major change in one area of your life, try and keep changes in other areas to a minimum.
3. Minimise uncertainty. Get as much information as possible.
4. Generate options so you, and others, have some choice and do not feel trapped.
5. Reward yourself, and others. Give yourself a treat.
6. Reduce or postpone non-essentials during major changes.
7. Ensure flexible respite, and rest periods.
8. Know the attitude of yourself and others towards change:

    Extraverts – Need the opportunity to discuss the situation fully with others.
    Introverts – Need written information, prior to any discussion. They need time to digest and reflect on all the implications of change.

    Factual people – Need detailed data, and specific examples of the proposed changes.
    Intuitive people – Need to see the broad implications, and the opportunities offered by the changes.

Analytical people – Need to be given logical reasons for the changes, and the timing involved.

'Heart' people – Need to know that personnel issues have been fully addressed.

Orderly people – Need a timetable of phased goals towards completing the changes.

Flexible people – Need sufficient leeway so they can use their initiative.

SEARCHING QUESTIONS

1. How many changes have you faced in the past twelve months? If it is more than two major ones (eg house move, job change, marriage, childbirth, divorce, bereavement) or several minor ones, try to have at least a whole year without further changes.

2. What small things are rewarding for you? (Eg special chocolates, a bottle of wine, a takeaway meal, a day out, a night in, a good read, a DVD.)
Make a list.

3. How good are you at giving yourself, and others, small rewards?

4. When did you last express appreciation to another person?

10. FALSE IMAGES OF GOD

Life is a journey punctuated by distinctive landmarks. Often these are unexpected discoveries that bear closer inspection. I sometimes wonder what would have happened if Moses had not gone over to look at the strange sight of a bush obviously on fire, and yet clearly not being burned up. It was precisely because he did go over and have a look that God spoke to him from within the bush.

'The unreflected life is not worth living,' said the Greek philosopher Socrates nearly 2,500 years ago, and it remains true today. The pace of life nowadays leaves little room for reflection and so we rush on, carrying with us partial and misleading notions, until something stops us in our tracks.

Nowhere is this more true than in our understanding, or frequently our misunderstanding, of God. We do not realise what a limited and often distorted inner image we have created for ourselves until something happens to bring the defective image to our notice. Whatever draws our attention to the distortion acts like sunlight glistening from a shard of glass lying on the ground. That broken piece may have been there a long time, half buried and dangerous, but until the sunlight draws attention to its presence it continues to be a danger.

The best way to detect false notions about God is by noticing the unexpected shafts of sunlight that reveal their presence. False notions are perilous because they limit our relationship with the Truth.

Many years ago, it suddenly occurred to me that God does not have 'off days'. That was a huge relief to me as I was praying about some matter that I had brought to Him countless times before. Now, I had never consciously formed the idea that God was capricious and that I must approach Him carefully. I had never realised that I was afraid of asking Him too much, or too often, or at the wrong moment – until that day when it came as such a release to me to realise that God does not have 'wrong moments'.

My enormous relief when the truth dawned that God does not change as we humans do, showed me that I must have been assuming that He did. I had previously been limited, and so had limited God, by the fear that He would change like our British weather, and I had better be similarly prepared. While my head knew that God is not fickle, my heart was unable to hear that message for many years.

It was not hard to trace that projection back to my childhood perception of my earthly father. In those far-off days there were times when it was definitely wise to keep out of the way, and to play at the farthest end of the garden. Many years later I was talking with a friend about what C.S. Lewis calls 'false half gods' limiting our spiritual growth. She said she did not think that she had any knocking around, but the next day she came into my room laughing. She had already found one by a sudden shaft of light glinting on a fleeting thought.

That very morning she had been reading in the Psalms about the righteousness of God, and praying for grace to be a righteous person. Quick as a flash had then come the thought 'But you'll soon catch me out'. She said that had it not been for our conversation the previous day she would have dismissed such an expectation as irrelevant. Now she realised that somewhere around for her, lurking and nearly buried, there was a false image of a Gotcha god, bent on catching her out.

There are many variants of that one. Some, mainly older, people realise that their perception of God is still being warped by a background image of the Village Policeman god, patrolling with the express purpose, it seems to them, of stopping youthful fun. Others can identify a vague, prowling fear of some Old Man in the Sky, often with a big stick with which to beat them.

In case you think that these impressions are hopelessly out of date I can assure you that they are constantly being made more culturally relevant. Some people realise that they are very wary of a god who seems to them the Great Examiner or the OFSTED Inspector. There is a definite standard to reach, a pass mark that must be attained. This notion grows uncorrected in the dark, inner recesses of the mind until the imagined standard is quite unreachable. The more technologically up to date even fear the god who, in their deepest being, they have come to regard as an All Seeing Eye in the sky. This Satellite god is continuously spying on them to see that they never make even an honest mistake. There is for them no escape from such hostile surveillance.

Whatever the imagery, the distorted notion is of being caught out and punished. It leaves no room for the true God who longs for His people to come into a living, developing relationship of trust based on love. Part of entering into that relationship is confession of genuine wrong doing and being. Sadly, the notion of a welcoming God with arms wide open to receive us is often marred and distorted by false half gods.

In her book *Driven Beyond the Call of God* Pamela Evans tells of how her son David

> had come to realise that he saw God as a commanding officer who required his obedience. Yes, he did know about God's love, but he didn't particularly feel the need to experience it. He saw it as a luxury – not really necessary for a good soldier. All God had to do was bark out the orders and he'd do as he was told. The love aspect was all very well but he could cope without it. … Over a period of a few weeks God graciously showed David in a variety of ways that He wanted to relate to him as a loving father, not as a commanding officer – that love was not an optional refinement to the relationship. *God is love!*[1]

Those who have had particularly unfortunate experiences in early life have sometimes named their false half god as a Tyrant, or a

Stern Judge. They have sadly formed the concept of someone who is indubitably about to throw the whole book of retribution at them. They understand the idea of Justice, but have unfortunately never seen the other side of the coin, which is the God of Mercy.

A friend once gave me a beautiful crystal ornament. Its owl shape is made up of many carved and polished facets. Because light penetrates them at different angles the varying parts reflect many colours, and every time I look at my ornament I see a different colour, and different combinations of colours. The eyes in particular are green when seen head on, but they are transformed into blues, greys and purples just by varying the viewing angle. What I see at any one time depends on which facet I am looking at, for I cannot see all of them at the same time. That owl to me is an apt illustration of how I can only comprehend a few of the many attributes of God at one time. There are so many facets to the incomprehensible Other that what I see depends on which aspect I am looking at, and relating to, on that specific day. All are true, but none is the whole truth. God Himself has not changed, but the aspect I may be seeing is not the same aspect as yesterday or last week. My understanding is limited and finite. He is infinite. We need to remind ourselves that there is so much more to the fullness of God than the particular facet we are engaging with at any one moment.

We are created in the image of God, who is always in relationship. The three Persons of the Trinity are a complementary Unity. Different analogies show us different aspects of God. All are true as far as they go, but none is the complete Truth. Some of our false images arise because we have adopted the prevailing 'Delete as applicable' approach of our push-button culture. We have endorsed the tick-list attitude of exclusion, instead of holding ourselves open to the entirety and immensity of God.

There are other false half gods that occur quite frequently and are worth looking out for. The Miser, or Paymaster General, from whom everything has to be well and truly earned. This is such a travesty of salvation by grace, freely offered, that this one is usually quite well buried, and hard to locate, but its influence remains until it is exposed.

Then there are a number of opposite images. The Father Christmas god, from whom we expect to get what we want. The Magician, a sort of divine Sooty who just waves a magic wand and things turn out in our favour. Sad variants of this are the Santa Claus who only brings goodies to good children; and the Fairy in the Grotto who brings goodies, but only to others. Then there is the Slot Machine god. You put in your money, whatever your chosen currency, and expect to get a particular result on demand. Or the Pinball Machine on the Pier, with the assumption that if you go on trying long enough you would be very unlucky not to get something back.

Another pair of opposites are the Frozen god and the Buddy god. The first is an abstract concept, without feelings and making it impossible to enter into a relationship. It is detached, cold, humourless and inanimate, a snowman of our own creation. But the opposite is just as much a travesty of the truth. The Good Buddy or Mr Nice Guy, who is always there when I want someone; always available; always smiling; always willing to overlook my shortcomings.

Some people have a long-buried concept of God as some sort of Puppet Master. For them He is someone who pulls all the strings. They assume that they themselves have no control over their lives, and therefore no responsibility either. A more sinister variant of this is the Slave Driver god who seems to be demanding ever more while caring and giving ever less. It is quite impossible to satisfy this one, or to begin any sort of relationship. It induces only fear and rebellion. At the other end of the spectrum is the god of Last Resort. This one is revealed by such comments as 'I've tried absolutely everything, the only thing I can do now is pray about it.'

Sometimes it is half-conscious images of oneself that, when examined, may reflect a hidden false image of God. To regard oneself as a Cinderella without a Fairy Godmother seems to suggest the assumption that God loves everyone – except me. The corollary of this is so often that I can love everyone else, but not myself. The image of God that results from this attitude to oneself is that God has favourites, and I am not one of them. That definitely needs some attention. It is a scriptural injunction to love one's neighbour as oneself, but I cannot recall ever hearing a sermon on Love Yourself. Dangerous, but essential stuff!

Some people struggle to be, or to become, omnicompetent. They have high standards of what is or 'ought' to be achievable in their chosen field. They try to be a one person band instead of a team player. I hope I shall never forget the quiet voice of the mentor with whom I was sharing some of my struggles at one time. It was salutary to hear, 'Ruth, just remember that you are not Mrs God'. Many times since, it has been most helpful to repeat that to myself whenever I have felt over burdened and weary of responsibility.

Then there is the Fix It god, a sort of Jimmy Saville in the sky, and the closely related Genie of the Lamp. The assumption here is that I will seek that god out only when I am in dire need, and I expect to get my needs met, or the situation put right, at once. In between such times, when all is going relatively smoothly and I can handle things, the lamp remains on the shelf, gathering dust. But it is handy to have it there, just in case of trouble.

The more modern version of this is the Remote Control god. If I press the right buttons, in the right sequence, then I will get the diversion I want. If that does not suit my needs I can change channels instantly, and frequently, without ever getting out of my comfortable chair.

In these days of knowledge explosion and information overkill there is a common misconception that we no longer 'need' to invoke the idea of any god, let alone God Almighty. He has been reduced to a mere god of the gaps, useful to fill in those areas where, as yet, we have no other explanation.

Once the partial, misleading or downright distorting images

of God are recognised, and owned, it is generally possible to spot how they were acquired. Once people are aware of their particular distortions and false half images of God it is as though the windows have been cleaned after a long, hard winter. At last they can see out, and they can see clearly, without mist and fogginess.

Children certainly pick up some interesting and highly individual concepts of God. One girl drew a beautiful picture of a giant tortoise. She had not stayed up late watching the old TV series *One Foot in the Grave*, but she had certainly misheard the person leading church services week after week. She tried to fit what she heard so invitingly every week into her own, as yet limited, experience. So she drew 'As our Saviour Tortoise' (taught us)! Then there was the boy who amazed his grandmother by praying to Harold. This turned out to be his interpretation of the old-fashioned phrase 'Hallowed be thy name'!

Both these children were quite naturally trying to make sense of what they heard, and so it had to fit into the constraints of their own limited exposure to life. Such quaint ideas are easy to recognise as distorted impressions. As the children grew in understanding and experience these ideas would soon be corrected. But the majority of misleading conclusions we infer about God, based on our early encounters with imperfect parental and other authority figures, are harder to recognise. Being only half true they still have some semblance to truth.

In Chapter 4 we saw the need to unpack the baggage we carry with us from our past experiences, in order to face the present uncontaminated with what has gone before. The same principle applies to our spiritual development. What is appropriate at the age of five is no longer so at fifteen. What may be healthy in childhood is no longer so at mid-life, much less old age. We need to be constantly updating our images and notions about the God who is the ground of our being, our source and resource.

Sometimes just the recognition that a false half god has flashed through our consciousness is enough to prompt some corrective thinking on the matter. The very admission that such submerged obstacles to mature faith actually do exist may be enough to disempower them.

At other times, the process will be enhanced by verbalising the dawning insights. It is often helpful to talk through any such discoveries with someone who is prepared to listen, really listen. That presupposes that the person we choose to confide in is prepared to join us on our voyage of discovery. We need their undivided and understanding attention to help us get in touch with our long-buried images, fantasies and fears. Only when we know what these are can we evaluate them as the adults we now are, and grow into a more mature and appropriate relationship with our Creator God.

Sometimes we can revise and develop our understanding of God by making two lists. One would enumerate all the positive attributes of our understanding of God; it would contain as much as we can conceptualise and express of who we understand God is. The other list would be a catalogue of what we now know to be false concepts. It would contain all those things that we now realise that God is not. Sometimes it is only by realising what we do not accept as true and valid that we can refine and define what we actually do believe.

It is always interesting, and sometimes very mind stretching, to realise that different groups of people actually respond quite naturally to very different aspects of God. All these aspects give a glimpse of the great I AM, but none by itself can begin to convey the immensity of the One who existed before the foundation of the world.

Some people relate most easily and naturally to the God of Truth and absolutes. The Divine Ruler, King and Judge are aspects of the Godhead that are most meaningful to them. Others respond more from the heart than the head. They are drawn by such concepts as God the Father, Abba; also Christ the Saviour, Redeemer and Shepherd.

For a mature faith we do need to develop an understanding and a relationship with both aspects, and much more, but our starting place will be different.

Whatever our starting place, we all need to track down and bring to the surface any false half gods. They prevent us developing a vibrant relationship with the living, loving God revealed in Jesus Christ His Son, through the Holy Spirit.

Do You Recognise Any of These False Half Gods?

Gotcha! Policeman
Great Examiner
Old Man with a Stick
OFSTED Inspector
Spy Satellite

Miser
Paymaster General
Santa Claus
Magician
Slot Machine
Pinball Machine

Snowman, or Warm Buddy
Puppet Master
Slave Driver
Commanding Officer
Mr Fix It
Remote Control
god of the gaps

SEARCHING QUESTIONS

1. Are there any ways in which your current image(s) of God need to change in order to reflect the true God?

Some of the things God is:
Longing to hear from us
Never too busy to listen
Colour blind
Able to take the strain
Too big for words
Always the same
Always ready to forgive
Always able to pick you up

Some of the things that God is not:
Exclusive
A last resort
Corruptible
A Trivial Pursuit
A crutch
A wet blanket
Put off by appearances
Happy to play second fiddle

2. Now add your own items to each of the above lists.

NOTE

1. Pamela Evans, *Driven Beyond the Call of God* (Oxford: Bible Reading Fellowship, 1999).

11. SLAVE DRIVER OR SHEPHERD?

Not long ago I met a man with a rare attitude for the twenty-first century. He was unusual because he had declined to accept promotion when it was offered to him. After much thought and prayer he had taken that decision because he realised that where he was happened to be just about the right fit for him. He had achieved that somewhat unusual situation of being a round peg in a round hole.

Roger told me that he found his present work interesting. It was varied, giving a reasonable balance of technical challenge and contact with people. He found himself stretched just enough to maintain his interest, but not so much that he had no energy left over for his family and friends, and his other interests. He was able to maintain a busy but not feverish role in his local church, and to play some part in other community activities.

To move just one notch up the ladder at work would have taken him out of the area where he was performing well and which gave him personal satisfaction. It would have involved more travelling, more management meetings, and generally more hassle all round. In short, he was likely to become a round peg trying to accommodate himself in an uncomfortably square hole. He realised that if he accepted the lure of promotion he would probably be exchanging work that suited his talents and his personality, for responsibilities and duties that did not.

Roger weighed up the situation, discussed it with his wife and close friends and somewhat reluctantly turned down the tempting offer. The increased salary and status within the organisation were a very real attraction. The downside was that the new position would have put him under relentless pressure at almost every point. He would have less time with his family, and much less opportunity and energy for his church and other activities. Roger chose to stay where he functioned well and was happy, rather than be pushed into work and a lifestyle that would be too pressurised most of the time, as well as having other uncongenial aspects to it.

In making his decision, Roger had chosen to follow the Shepherd who leads His flock, rather than allowing himself to be driven on by other powerful forces. It is only butchers who get behind the flock and drive them on to their destruction. A shepherd sees that his flock has good grass to eat, enough for all. He finds still waters for them to drink from, for sheep cannot drink from turbulent waters. He sees that the sheep are kept safe from predatory wild animals and sheep stealers.

There are two widely divergent attitudes to work that lie at opposite ends of a continuum, with most of us being neither at one extreme nor the other. However, some people do seem to be letting their lives be ruled by one of these attitudes, while at the same time, deep in their hearts, they wish they had just a little more of the alternative one.

The drop-out element of society appear to despise conventional work as a burden. In their view, the commitment to work for someone else, to be under any authority, to keep prescribed hours and to do defined tasks, is an insurmountable barrier to their own human fulfilment. At the other end of the line are those who elevate the function of work so that it becomes synonymous with life itself. It becomes the mainspring of their being, the reason for their very existence. They use it as the vehicle for both personal and social fulfilment so that some of them, when the time comes, literally retire and die. If they do not actually die, many sadly seem to die within themselves, for they have no other source of meaning, no other resources to keep them going.

The first group have themselves as the centre of their existence. Their relationships are often somewhat shallow, being centred on themselves, their own wishes, needs and values. The second group are equally in danger of having impoverished lives. They have fallen into the opposite trap of using work to protect them from the necessity to engage, on a personal level, with people and with wider social issues.

When we carry with us into the present a lot of baggage from the past it is tempting to shelve unresolved relationship problems by adopting one or other of these polarities. The problems do not really go away. They are merely stored away in a more or less forgotten lumber room. The trouble with this method of dealing with difficulties is that every now and then some of the contents of that junk room spill over into the living room and can no longer be ignored. If the occupant decides not to notice them, other people surely will!

Many people today are allowing themselves to be driven along paths that are not going to lead to good grazing lands, and which offer very little opportunity to drink from the Water of Life. Workaholism is a disease of our time. People work long hours, some even go in at weekends and many take work home. On every commuter train a few sleep, some read the paper or a book, but very many work. Where there is room, there are spreadsheets in evidence, bundles of papers being perused and feverishly annotated. There is always the 'click click' of busy laptops punctuated by the trilling of numerous mobile phones.

Greater productivity and ever higher standards are being required in every workplace today. It seems as though more is always being demanded of people who are in employment. If they do not prove satisfactory in their job there is the continual spectre that they may be eased out of their position, if not thrown out. Rationalisation of working practices, reorganisations and take-overs are commonplace. There is no longer an assured career path, and no automatic pay rise.

The external reality is bad enough, but the inner drive that compels people to put work above every other aspect of life does far more damage. When people attempt to get all their satisfaction and gratification from their employment, it is not surprising that work-related activities and colleagues soon become a substitute for the family and a wider social life. The non-work people to whom they have a responsibility soon begin to realise that they are given a very much lower priority than anything and anybody connected with work.

This state of affairs has got much worse since the advent of email, laptops and mobile phones. One woman said to me very bitterly, 'The trouble is that there are three in our marriage now, and the third is that computer.' Everywhere they went, the laptop came with them. Instead of talking with each other as they travelled, he talked with someone else via email. Sometimes the 'he' is, of course, a 'she'; men are not the only ones who hide behind electronic gadgets.

When human relationships are marginalised like this there is a chain reaction of unhappiness. This impels people to bury their inner pain in ever more work in their search for fulfilment. Those in employment spend more time and energy in that direction, while those at home can become just as workaholic on the domestic scene or in voluntary work.

Another story told by Pamela Evans in her book *Driven Beyond the Call of God* is of Rachel who was driven to care for others, and wrote,

> In the end my frenzied activity led to burn-out ... Even to this day I feel (rather like an alcoholic) that I'm only one step away from the workaholic treadmill. I still feel more comfortable with people if I'm fulfilling some need. I haven't yet learned how to relate securely without a role, but I'm asking the Lord to lead me on in this.[1]

Work, in the sense of completing specific tasks, has always been a part of the life of humankind. It is designed to be a part, not the whole, of life. The Lord God put Adam in the Garden of Eden 'to work it and take care of it'. He knew that work only, and alone, was insufficient, and gave Eve to Adam as a helper suitable for him. Work was a part of their life, but was not a burden. Toil and shame came with disobedience and rebellion against God.

As I said earlier, many people today have elevated work from being just one aspect of the rhythm of life, to being synonymous with life itself. It is as though the value of a person, and their prestige, are defined by the role they play more than by who they are. Whenever my brother and I spoke of our friends at school, one of our parents would inevitably ask, 'What does his/her father do?' That seemed to them to be of more importance than what sort of a person his child, our friend, was and it irritated us both.

When work takes over and becomes the predominant part of life, to the detriment of relationships, and especially of relationship with God, then sooner or later it will lead to confusion. When it becomes all important, even to being in competition with God Himself – as in the building of the tower of Babel (Gen. 11:1–9) – it clearly has become idolatrous.

Despite this, many Christians today are workaholics. They have unwittingly become obsessively addicted to work. That notion of addiction comes from a Latin word which more or less means being 'given over', or awarded to, someone else. In this case it is something rather than someone else, just as a debtor could by Roman law be given over to become the slave of his creditor. He would no longer be a free agent, he would have no choice but to obey his new master.

Addicts are people who try to escape from the reality of their situation, and to anaesthetise their inner pain, dissatisfaction, loneliness or other unhappiness, by throwing themselves into any one of a number of substitute activities. Computer games, gambling and any number of high speed, high risk activities can all give a 'buzz', a 'high', to distract the addict from something he cannot solve or face. They are known as process addictions, to distinguish them from the more widely recognised chemical addiction of substance misuse. But any addiction is still addiction, and one of its characteristics is that it induces personal blindness to what is really going on. Addicts deny to themselves and to others that they are 'given over' to a particular behaviour. Workaholics in particular deny that work, and all it stands for, now rules their lives.

Many people today are mastered by, rather than being masters of, their work. This is not only the case in secular work. Ministers of all denominations, and leaders in a number of Christian organisations, are alarmingly prone to workaholism. In the twenty-first century it is sad to note that some of our churches are busy, overactive, driven communities. There are many meetings, but precious little time or opportunity for the actual meeting of person with person, all roles laid aside.

Even as I was about to start writing this chapter I asked someone how his ministerial training weekend had been for him. He pulled a face, reflected momentarily and then said, 'There was too much spirituality in it.' I asked what he would have liked to have had instead, and he said that he would have liked more practical things such as how to take different types of services. His emphasis was all on the 'doing' part of life, with little attention to the 'being' aspect, and apparently no time for reflection on what life is really about.

When work overrides all other aspects of life it tends to become destructive. It destroys relationships, and ultimately health. Unwaged work can be equally destructive.

It was a great day when Jesus interrupted His journey to drop in at the home kept and run by Martha. He had much on His mind, for He was on His way to Jerusalem, where torture and death were waiting for Him. At that moment He was probably wanting some respite from all the pressures He was under, a sanctuary from the crowds who jostled and pushed and vied for His attention. I fancy that a quiet sit down and a sandwich, or a bowl of soup with His friends, would have met His needs.

What Jesus could have done with at that time was someone

to listen to Him for a change. He had travelled far, on foot, and met the varying needs of countless people. Now He was in need of an understanding and sympathetic reception.

He did not get it. Martha was delighted to see Him and wanted to give the very best that she could muster at short notice. There were no freezers or fridges then. A few hens scratching in the courtyard, probably, and some vegetables and herbs growing nearby. She bustled about, trying to do honour (as she saw it) to the occasion, and to her special visitor; and she had to do it her way. She overdid it. She became distracted by all her self-imposed preparations that she considered just had to be undertaken. It would have been unthinkable for her to sit down and just be with Him. No, she saw her role as being to rush about and do all the things that had to be done. She was doing it all for Him. She was trying to be kind, but her brand of kindness was not what the Lord required at that moment.

Worse still, Martha became increasingly irritated with her sister who she saw as neglecting her duty. Mary ought surely to have been helping her out in the kitchen at the back. There was just so much to get done. Mary should have been fulfilling her obvious obligations and serving the Lord, instead of just sitting there!

Martha allowed herself to get very upset at what, from her point of view, was a gross dereliction of duty. No amount of beckoning and calling made any impression on Mary, she just went on sitting there. She was listening to Jesus' needs, His preoccupations, and was quite oblivious of her sister. I can imagine Martha's increasing anger and despair; so much to do and her own sister not lifting a finger or lending a hand, just sitting there.

Martha's need to have everything just right finally spilled over and she complained to Jesus, and then she appealed to Him to intervene. She was feeling bitter about her sister's behaviour, and she also felt let down by Jesus. Surely He should know what a lot she was having to do, all on her own! 'Don't you care that my sister has left me to do the work by myself? Tell her to help me!' But at least Martha did give voice, and to the right person, to her feelings of frustration and anger; she did not let them just build up inside her.

Jesus was in all probability weary, and it is likely that He was also troubled. He knew what was waiting for Him in the days ahead, and just for now He wanted a little oasis of peace. Instead, He found Himself in the midst of a domestic dispute. He loved Martha, but on this occasion it was Mary who had chosen the better thing to do, which was to just be. It was more important to be with Him than to be rushing around doing things for Him, things that at that moment He did not require.

A great deal of the teaching that Jesus gave was delivered in the form of parables, and I believe that the story of Martha and Mary is itself a parable for us today. Most of us have both a Martha and a Mary side, and both of them need to be nurtured. It is not a case of loving one and hating or despising the other. It is a matter of knowing when an active, interventionist approach is really required by the situation we are in, and when a somewhat more reflective, thoughtful stance would be more suitable. We need to recognise when it is right to take an active role, when it is appropriate for us to initiate and carry through some undertaking, and when it is necessary to plan and pursue goals. Some people find it hard to do all this without also hounding and pursuing other people in the process.

We also need to know when a more deliberative, hands off, waiting and watching approach would be a more helpful one, and would fit the actual situation better. It is a matter of knowing what we can do, and whether it is right that those things should be done, and done now; and whether or not we are the ones to do them, given all the circumstances.

When we are all busy and bustling we wear ourselves out, and frequently annoy those around whom we choose to bustle. All sitting, listening and looking but taking little active part, and we might be in danger of shirking those things that really are our responsibility. So it is not a case of being wholly Martha-ish, or of always being in the Mary mode, but of discerning which form of response is appropriate in any given situation, and then bringing that one into operation. All Martha, and little gets properly thought through; all Mary, and little gets done.

Not long ago I was talking with a busy, active woman, who seemed to me to be very much the 'Girl Guide helping an old woman across the road' type. It was her inner need to be needed, her own desire to feel good because she had done something for someone else, that caused her to be so busy. Like the caricature of a Girl Guide she did not stop to find out whether the old woman really wanted to cross the road. If she saw one hovering near a pedestrian crossing she was inclined to impel her over, no matter what.

Molly told me very firmly, and without any shadow of doubt in her voice, that the Lord needed far more Marthas than Marys. She had missed the point. The story makes it very plain, indeed it is explicitly stated, that Jesus loved both the sisters. However, only one chose to do what was actually needed at that particular time.

As I watch frenzied commuters I wonder about their image of God. Do they, I muse, half-consciously consider Him to be a slave driver, relentlessly moving them on, always urging them to do more, and to do it more speedily. I ponder how differently some of them might be living if they were going at the more measured pace of a shepherd. Moreover, how life might be for them if they were relying on the Shepherd to be in charge of their lives. Jesus said, 'I am the good shepherd; I know my sheep and my sheep know me' (John 10:14).

The Shepherd desires that we know Him in our hearts, as well as with our heads. We must dare to be emotionally as well as intellectually engaged as we read Scripture. The living word has to become personal and experiential, as well as objectively factual. We have to let head and heart, Martha and Mary, each play their own part in our lives.

SEARCHING QUESTIONS

1. Is your god a slave driver, or a shepherd?

2. Do you work to live, or live to work?

3. Are you driven to do things, or do you choose to do them?

4. Read one of the following passages several times, slowly and reflectively. Have you let it descend from your head into your heart?

- God is not heard, or served, in the hurricane, or earthquake, but in a gentle whisper (1 Kings 19:11–12). Slow down your inner pace, and listen for it.
- Wait quietly (Lam. 3:22–33).
- Allow yourself to be renewed (Ezek. 36:25–27).
- Walk hand in hand with your Shepherd (Isa. 41:13, 42:6).
- Hear Him call you by name, whatever your circumstances (Isa. 43:1–7).
- When the going gets tough He will carry you through (Isa. 46:3–4).
- Remember you are engraved on the palms of His hands (Isa. 49:15–16).

NOTE

1. Pamela Evans, *Driven Beyond the Call of God* (Oxford: Bible Reading Fellowship, 1999).

12. CONSIDER THE LILIES

Going at the pace of the shepherd, rather than being driven by that internal slave driver so many of us have acquired, we will have time to look around, wonder and enjoy the present moment. That is all we can be sure of, and that is where God is. His name is 'I AM', not 'I was'; so we need to leave our mistakes and regrets at the foot of the cross, and live fully in today. His name is not 'I will be'; so the problems and fears of the future, the unproductive worryings that hound us all from time to time, must be surrendered too. When we live in the present moment we are most fully present to the 'I AM'.

The subject of leisure is the Cinderella of topics in Christian considerations, despite the booming leisure industry. Apart from a few notable exceptions, like clowns and storytellers, it seems to be the Cinderella whose fairy godmother has been hijacked. This Cinderella languishes, cold and neglected by charred, grey, cheerless ashes. She merits only the grudging leftovers, the remnants of time and attention when more worthy subjects have been fully attended to. Like the Ugly Sisters, work and duty are seldom satisfied, so there is little left over for her.

A friend of mine, knowing of my interest in the subject, ran a library search in the Christian college where she was then working. There were something like 120 listings on work, but nothing on leisure. True, there were 12 on holidays, but most of those were on things like how to run a Holiday Club. Fun for the children, certainly, but not leisure for the leaders! Recreation, even when spelt re-creation, did not get a mention, it was clearly not a credible subject.

The creation story in the first chapter of Genesis is notable for the constant rhythm of work, and rest from work. This illustrates the ideal pattern of work and rest following one another repeatedly. Together they form a complementary rhythm of life.

What is illustrated here is much more than passive resting. It is fair to infer that there was positive enjoyment in that rest. After each spate of creative activity there was a definite break, frequently a review of what had been accomplished, and always the refrain 'And God saw that it was good'.

The problem for us is that work and leisure compete for our time and our energy. 'Work' embraces all those things that we have to do, in order to live. It includes not only those things for which we are paid, but all the other necessities like school runs and essential travel; the requirements of running a home, and looking after oneself generally. 'Leisure' includes all those enriching, pleasurable activities which are discretionary, not obligatory. They are the things about which we have real choices.

Generally speaking, at work we earn money and our leisure pursuits tend to consume it. Often this adds to the guilt many people feel at taking time off work for something so 'unproductive' as leisure. But leisure is so much more than 'not working', or not getting paid for what we do. It is a travesty of the Christian faith to stress only work and worship. The elements of rich enjoyment, and of adequate relaxation for all, are surely the other side of the coin.

True leisure needs to be defined in terms of the value it adds to life, the quality it bestows on our lives. It embodies a sense of being, as well as of doing. When Pooh asked Christopher Robin how you do nothing, he got the reply, 'It means going along, and listening to all those things you can't hear, and not bothering' (A.A. Milne, *House at Pooh Corner*). The aspect of 'not bothering' is an essential antidote to a life of care and 'getting things done'. The poet W.H. Davies put it another way when he wrote: 'What is this life if full of care, we have no time to stand and stare …'

Jesus told people to, 'Look at the birds of the air' and to 'See how the lilies of the field grow' (Matt. 6:26,28). Our busy lives need space for reflection; time to do nothing in particular, to just be.

They also need time for activities of our choice. For some this will be active sport, drama or other energetic, and perhaps gregarious, pursuits. For others it may be a more sedentary occupation, perhaps something reflective, artistic or educational to fill out what is missing in the obligatory work and chores aspect of life.

As heads and tails are two aspects of a single coin, so work and leisure need to go together. One without the other is meaningless. They are designed to balance each other. Leisure is needed to fill out, to fulfil, those aspects of life that are not utilised in our work. As human beings we have social, aesthetic and cultural needs, as well as physical and spiritual ones. We have the need to be stretched, and to relax; to be interested and stimulated, and also to switch off at times. Neither work nor leisure alone can adequately satisfy all these aspects of a person.

So we see that leisure is an essential ingredient for a complete life, and must not be regarded as in any way an optional extra. Jesus said that He came not only to give life to those who accept and follow Him, but that His followers might have it 'to the full' (John 10:10). Other translations say 'more abundantly'. This implies an extra dimension that imparts a reason for living; a sense of purpose that gives a vitality and a zing to life. It is the difference between existence, and life.

We must beware of reducing life merely to the utilitarian. It is noteworthy that the original garden had 'trees that were pleasing to the eye' as well as for food (Gen. 2:9). We are unlikely to give adequate attention to leisure unless we grasp the fact that pleasure, pure pleasure, is part of the creation ordinance of God. It is part of His very nature, and we are made in His image. Part of the problem is the false distinction that has grown up between that which is sacred, and those things that are considered secular. The priest-poet David Adam, the Iona Community and others have done a great service in drawing attention back to the Celtic understanding of the unity of life.

Somewhere along the way we have lost the art, the craftsmanship, of really living. We need to capture the concept of being skilled at crafting our lives, so that in their entirety they are pleasing works of art. Pleasing to us and to our Master Craftsman. Each aspect of life needs to receive loving attention, and all facets must fit well together, so that they come together as a satisfying and attractive whole.

This is surely the idea behind Proverbs 8:30:

> **Then I was the craftsman at his side.**
> **I was filled with delight day after day,**
> **rejoicing always in his presence,**
> **rejoicing in his whole world**
> **and delighting in mankind.**

The Jerusalem Bible has a significant additional thought about this craftsmanship. That same verse (my italics) reads 'I was by his side, a master craftsman, delighting Him day by day, *ever at play in his presence, at play* everywhere in his world, delighting to be with the sons of men.'

One of the reasons why we are not able to live out our inheritance of *abundant* life is surely because many of us have forgotten how to play. We are too serious for too much of the time, without any let up. The ability to be totally absorbed in their play is one of the characteristics of children, as every parent knows, especially when it comes to bedtime! And we have been warned that unless we emulate children, and become as they are, we cannot enter the kingdom of heaven. We need to get totally absorbed in some recreational activity, just for its own sake, at regular intervals.

The essence of leisure is freedom. Much of our time goes on regular commitments, on those things that we are paid, or called, to do. We have to be very sure indeed about that 'call' bit, and check it out with wise mentors. It is easy to drive ourselves or allow others to drive us, in ways, and into places, that are not of God. He desires mercy and not sacrifice (Hosea 6:6); mercy towards those of our own family, rather than escaping from domestic obligations while we 'sacrifice' ourselves, and them, with other duties.

Another slice of time goes on sheer maintenance, on such things as eating, sleeping, hygiene, essential travelling and running of the home. Some must also be apportioned for worship and fellowship. To live as God intended us to, we must also reserve both time and energy for the things that resource us, and the things that recharge our personal batteries.

When we try and keep going without regular breaks, we are definitely going against the Maker's instructions. That is both disobedience, and arrogance. God Himself rested on the seventh day and was refreshed (Exod. 31:17, RSV). We are made in His image, and we too need the equivalent of a Sabbath-rest. We need seasons of refreshment at more or less consistent intervals, and if we do not take them we are surely implying that we are more capable than our Maker!

Many people today, especially in senior positions, do not have regular schedules. In these international, global village days, business meetings often require them to drop everything and travel abroad at short notice. On their return, some go straight to the office to report in person, and then carry on without a break. There is a real need for them, and those who set their schedules, to adopt a policy of 'recovery time'. This should be budgeted for, and insisted on, after any period of extra strenuous exertion or prolonged work without an adequate restorative break.

People of old were much more sensible about this. When some of the Israelites were making the long trek on foot back to their homeland after generations in exile, it is recorded in Ezra 8:32, 'So we arrived in Jerusalem, where we rested three days'. They knew about the need for proper recovery, before pitching into the next phase of work and readjustment.

Chronic fatigue means that many people have come to accept that being only half alive is the norm for them, for their situation or for their type of work. Christians are told to offer themselves 'as *living* sacrifices' (Rom. 12:1), and yet today many are content to offer themselves, partially dead, for the service of God. The Old Testament makes it abundantly clear that imperfect or blemished sacrifices are not acceptable; they will be rejected.

Chronic fatigue is also highly inefficient. When people are tired they have to put in more effort, they make more mistakes and generally take longer to achieve slightly less. What a waste all round! It is poor stewardship of time and talent. One president of the USA had the right idea. He refused to sign any important document after 4pm. He rightly held that 'A tired mind rarely makes good decisions'.

The paradox is that it takes more discipline to stop and take time off, than it does to keep going in the same old way. Leisure is necessary to provide an escape from the pressures of work, and to give an opportunity for some other pursuit. While engaged in something quite different, all those faculties that have been engaged in work can be temporarily switched off. This interlude of 'shut down' ensures that pressing preoccupations somehow shake down, and when work is resumed they are generally seen in better perspective.

The right use of leisure bestows far more positive advantages than just restoring the status quo. It furnishes time and space for reflection; for learning from successes and failures alike; and for considering 'how the lilies of the field grow' (Matt. 6:28). It helps us to see our concerns within the wider cosmic context, and specifically with the eyes, the mind and the heart of God.

Many of us need to regain that sense of wide-eyed wonder that is characteristic of small children. We need to refrain from our headlong, blinkered, hurrying mentality, to pause and allow ourselves to see the beauty and the goodness in the world. It is there all around us, despite the natural and man-engendered disasters that fill our television screens. To keep our sanity we need to cease from our preoccupation with the horrors that do exist, and see also what is worthy and wonderful. We need to rest, as God did, and take time to see the good around us. Allow yourself to pick more daisies.

Leisure also provides an opportunity to engage that half of our brain that is not utilised in our everyday activities. For most of us this is the non-rational, non-verbal right side which deals with spatial relationships rather than with linear logic and analysis. Music, movement, the visual arts, metaphor, humour and all that goes to make up culture need their rightful place in our lives. Their place as of right, and not just the leftovers.

In our acquisitive age we need more than ever to have a definite boundary around our work, a limit to our acquisitiveness. Leisure has to do with the quality of life; it is involved with those things that go beyond the merely utilitarian, and it goes deeper than concerns with productivity. We do have to be engaged in those things but our humanity demands that we are involved in more than them alone.

'There is a time for everything, and a season for every activity under heaven.' Ecclesiastes 3 verse 1 does not add 'except leisure', though many Christians seem to live as though that caveat was emblazoned in the very heavens themselves. Sadly it has become engraved in many hearts, and is one of the old tape recordings that need to be erased, and replaced. This is part of the baggage from our past that needs attention and updating.

Many psalms in particular speak about the place of sheer delight, in the heart of God, and in the response of humankind. Leisure gives us the opportunity to do things for no other reason than that we delight to do them. It involves taking positive pleasure in things and actions, for their own intrinsic sake. It has to do with the good things, the abundance of life, with taking joy and being satisfied. It allows us the opportunity to reflect and to be refreshed in every part of our being.

We must beware lest we harbour some sort of celestial Scrooge in a dark corner of our belief system. The true God 'richly provides us with everything for our ENJOYMENT' (1 Tim. 6:17, my emphasis). Leisure does not just happen; we have to take steps to see that there is ring-fenced space for it in our diaries, and that we use them positively. It is a vital ingredient of a fully lived life, and not an optional extra. Like vitamins, we do not need a vast amount, but we do need it regularly as it cannot be stored and we suffer insidiously when we have a deficiency.

Leisure Is:

1. A creation ordinance, not an optional extra.
2. Able to add quality to life through social, aesthetic, artistic and cultural activities.
3. Complementary to work.
4. An escape from the pressures of work.
5. An opportunity to get many issues in perspective.
6. That which enables us to be fully alive, not half dead much of the time.
7. Essential to life. Like vitamins, it must be taken regularly, and cannot be stored.

SEARCHING QUESTIONS

1. Is leisure your Cinderella?
2. Does it merit a regular, prospective entry in your diary?
3. When did you last play, or do anything for the sheer enjoyment of doing it?
4. Are you becoming skilled in the craft of living life abundantly?

FURTHER READING

Part One

England, Edward, *The Addiction of a Busy Life* (Crowborough: Aviemore Books, 1998).

Warren & Toll, *The Stress Workbook* (London: Nicholas Brealey Publishing, 1997).

Part Two

Fowke, Ruth, *Personality and Prayer* (Farnham: CWR, 2008).

Goldsmith and Wharton, *Knowing Me – Knowing You, Exploring Personality Type* (London: SPCK, 1993).

Part Three

Evans, Pamela, *Driven Beyond the Call of God* (Oxford: Bible Reading Fellowship, 1999).

Nash, Wanda, *Come Let us Play* (London: Darton, Longman & Todd, 1999).

Ryken, Leyland, *Work and Leisure in Christian Perspective* (Leicester: IVP, 1987).

Day and Residential Courses
Counselling Training
Leadership Development
Biblical Study Courses
Regional Seminars
Ministry to Women
Daily Devotionals
Books and Videos
Conference Centre

Trusted all Over the World

CWR HAS GAINED A WORLDWIDE reputation as a centre of excellence for Bible-based training and resources. From our headquarters at Waverley Abbey House, Farnham, England, we have been serving God's people for over 40 years with a vision to help apply God's Word to everyday life and relationships. The daily devotional *Every Day with Jesus* is read by nearly a million readers an issue in more than 150 countries, and our unique courses in biblical studies and pastoral care are respected all over the world. Waverley Abbey House provides a conference centre in a tranquil setting.

For free brochures on our seminars and courses, conference facilities, or a catalogue of CWR resources, please contact us at the following address:
CWR, Waverley Abbey House, Waverley Lane, Farnham, Surrey GU9 8EP, UK

Telephone: **+44 (0)1252 784700**
Email: **mail@cwr.org.uk**
Website: **www.cwr.org.uk**

CWR Applying God's Word
to everyday life and relationships

National Distributors

UK: (and countries not listed below)
CWR, Waverley Abbey House, Waverley Lane, Farnham, Surrey GU9 8EP.
Tel: (01252) 784700 Outside UK (44) 1252 784700

AUSTRALIA: KI Entertainment, Unit 31 317-321 Woodpark Road, Smithfield,
New South Wales 2164. Tel: 02 9604 3600 Fax: 02 9604 3699

CANADA: David C Cook Distribution Canada, PO Box 98,
55 Woodslee Avenue, Paris, Ontario N3L 3E5. Tel: 1800 263 2664

GHANA: Challenge Enterprises of Ghana, PO Box 5723, Accra.
Tel: (021) 222437/223249 Fax: (021) 226227

HONG KONG: Cross Communications Ltd, 1/F, 562A Nathan Road, Kowloon.
Tel: 2780 1188 Fax: 2770 6229

INDIA: Crystal Communications, 10-3-18/4/1, East Marredpalli, Secunderabad
– 500026, Andhra Pradesh. Tel/Fax: (040) 27737145

KENYA: Keswick Books and Gifts Ltd, PO Box 10242-00400, Nairobi.
Tel: (254) 20 312639/3870125

MALAYSIA: Salvation Book Centre (M) Sdn Bhd, 23 Jalan SS 2/64,
47300 Petaling Jaya, Selangor. Tel: (03) 78766411/78766797
Fax: (03) 78757066/78756360

Canaanland, No. 25 Jalan PJU 1A/41B, NZX Commercial Centre, Ara Jaya,
47301 Petaling Jaya, Selangor. Tel: (03) 7885 0540/1/2 Fax: (03) 7885 0545

NIGERIA: FBFM, Helen Baugh House, 96 St Finbarr's College Road,
Akoka, Lagos. Tel: (01) 7747429/4700218/825775/827264

PHILIPPINES: OMF Literature Inc, 776 Boni Avenue, Mandaluyong City.
Tel: (02) 531 2183 Fax: (02) 531 1960

SINGAPORE: Alby Commercial Enterprises Pte Ltd, 95 Kallang Avenue
#04-00, AIS Industrial Building, 339420. Tel: (65) 629 27238 Fax: (65) 629 27235

SOUTH AFRICA: Struik Christian Books, 80 MacKenzie Street, PO Box 1144,
Cape Town 8000. Tel: (021) 462 4360 Fax: (021) 461 3612

SRI LANKA: Christombu Publications (Pvt) Ltd, Bartleet House,
65 Braybrooke Place, Colombo 2. Tel: (9411) 2421073/2447665

USA: David C Cook Distribution Canada, PO Box 98, 55 Woodslee Avenue,
Paris, Ontario N3L 3E5, Canada. Tel: 1800 263 2664

For email addresses, visit the CWR website: www.cwr.org.uk

CWR is a Registered Charity – Number 294387

CWR is a Limited Company registered in England – Registration Number 1990308

Develop a more vibrant relationship with God

Personality and Prayer

What you have learned about praying may be your biggest hindrance to a natural, enjoyable prayer life – one that matches your preferred ways of communicating.

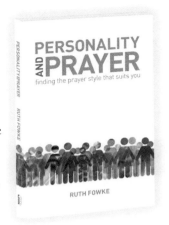

In *Personality and Prayer* Dr Ruth Fowke will help you discover the ways, places and times to pray that best suit your personality – and your changing needs.

by Ruth Fowke
100-page softback, 129x197mm
ISBN: 978-1-85345-488-2
£6.99 (plus p&p)

The perfect companion to *Personality and Stress*

Insight into Stress

Based on CWR's popular Insight seminar on stress, this book looks in depth at the subject of stress, enabling you to recognise stress-related problems and cope with the demands and expectations of yourself and others.

Helpful diagrams, biblical and individual case studies and personal application will deepen your understanding of stress and how to manage it, whether for your own benefit or for helping others.

by Beverley Shepherd
112-page hardback, 97x129mm
ISBN: 978-1-85345-384-7
£7.50 (plus p&p)

Available online at **www.cwrstore.org.uk** or from your local Christian bookseller.

Prices correct at time of printing.

UNDERSTANDING YOURSELF, UNDERSTANDING OTHERS

Eye-opening activities and powerful insights in a one-day seminar

This popular Waverley course using the Myers-Briggs Type Indicator™ will help you see what makes you and others tick – how people perceive the world and make decisions, and their preferred ways of thinking and acting.

Understanding our unique personality and our preferences can really help us in our personal and spiritual growth.

And understanding our differences can help us relate better to others and communicate more effectively.

You will learn some surprising things about your God-created personality, and see ways to reduce friction and minimise misunderstanding.

Visit **www.cwr.org.uk** for course dates or to book your place.

'CWR's training has been fantastic – rich and profound. It has touched me at many levels.'

™ Registered trademarks of Consulting Psychologists Press Inc. Oxford Psychologists Press Ltd has exclusive rights to the trademark in the UK.